S0-AGW-727

To: Lisa

From: Your @Amme

2014

Raising
PIGS

Raising
PIGS

*Share Your Garden with Some
Rooting, Snuffling Friends*

LEE FABER

Abbeydale Press

© Copyright 2009 Bookmart Limited

All rights reserved.
No part of this publication may be reproduced,
stored in a retrieval system or transmitted by
any means, electronic, mechanical, photocopying
or otherwise, without the prior permission in
writing of the publisher.

Published by Abbeydale Press
an imprint of Bookmart Ltd
Registered number 2372865
Trading as Bookmart Ltd
Blaby Road, Wigston, Leicester
LE18 4SE, England

Produced by Omnipress Limited, UK
Cover design by Omnipress Limited, UK

THE AUTHOR

LEE FABER is a native-born American who became a
British citizen, having been in the UK since 1981. She
has lived and worked in New York, Florida and London,
and now resides in Wiltshire. During her career she has
been involved in book editing and writing with an
emphasis on health, food and cookery. She has
specialised in Americanizing/Anglicising books on a
variety of subjects for both US and UK publishers. She
is also the author of *Healthy Oils, Aloe Vera, Berries,
Juices and Smoothies* and *Beginner's Guide to
Chickens* in this series. Lee is an accomplished cook
and has created many recipes.

PUBLISHER'S NOTE

Although the advice and information in this book
are believed to be accurate and true at the time
of going to press, neither the authors nor the
publisher can accept any legal responsibility or
liability for any errors or omissions that may be
made nor for any inaccuracies nor for any harm or
injury that comes about from following instructions
or advice in this book.

CONTENTS

INTRODUCTION

WHY? THE RATIONALE FOR RAISING PIGS

There are two rationales for raising pigs — they are intelligent, sweet-natured animals and can be both wonderful pets and wholesome food. Many people who keep pigs don't have a problem thinking about them as pork, unless they get overly attached to them, as did a friend of mine. She lives on a farm that rears its pigs for meat. One of her sows had a new litter. Amongst the babies was a runt who was not expected to live. Jane couldn't just let the poor thing die, so she decided to intervene, feeding the piglet goat's milk, first with an eye dropper, then with a baby's bottle. The piglet thrived and is now a cherished family pet, along with a few assorted dogs and cats. This pig will never become a pork chop.

Many people who raise pigs at home do so because they have the space; are fed up with supermarket prices; want more flavourful and tender pork; and want good food they have had a hand in rearing themselves. The fact that raising pigs can be fun is just a wonderful bonus.

Then there are people who think of pigs only as pets, like my daughter in Florida who has always wanted a pig. She's had hamsters and gerbils and cats and reptiles and currently has dogs. She said the three dogs — boxweiler, mastiff and bulldog — would accept a pig as another dog, and told her husband she needed a pig so she could help me with my research. He saw through that ploy saying, 'maybe she'll write a book about motorcycles and I can help her'. They are now at an impasse.

The truism is if you give your pig a happy life, it will bring you lots of enjoyment, both in its lifetime and afterwards.

There are some considerations to take into account before you run out and buy pigs. You must have enough land to raise a pig or two, you must have proper housing, but most important, even if you want only one pig as a pet, you must check with your local council and make sure there are no laws keeping you from doing so. In addition, you should read your deeds or lease to see if there are any restrictions about pets or livestock.

The Myths: pigs are inherently dirty and smelly, are gluttons and eat rubbish.

The Facts: pigs do not have an affinity for mud. They don't have any sweat glands, along with rhinos and hippos, so in very hot weather they tend to wallow in muddy water to cool off. In confined areas and around feeding and watering equipment, while rooting around, their pointy little hooves tear at the ground creating muddy areas.

Their rooting activity also sullies their image. When pigs were wild, they had to forage in the forest for nourishment (fruits and nuts fallen from trees, grubs, worms and other natural foodstuffs).

Since this is an inborn trait, pigs still supplement their diets in pastures, but it is no longer a necessity.

People use the expression 'eating like a pig' to denote gluttony. Pigs aren't actually greedy — growing pigs are fed to consume roughly 3% of their body weight daily. A normal sized adult male would have to eat about 2.5 kg (5.4 lb) of food to match this.

Pigs are not eaters of swill and rubbish as they have often been depicted. In olden days they would root through the lanes of rural villages, but they were searching for table scraps, mill waste and spilled grain, rather than garbage.

CHARACTERISTICS OF PIGS

As I mentioned earlier, pigs are intelligent and sweet-natured. Because of their innate smartness and desire to please, they are easier to train than cats or dogs. Pigs will respond to the human voice and will 'talk' to you, in the same way as your dogs will. They may even kiss you. They certainly like being scratched — in some cases to relieve the itch caused by insects and skin afflictions, but sometimes just because they are affectionate. Pigs also like toys, even though their interest span is very short. Pigs have good hearing, poor eyesight, beautiful long eyelashes and can run as fast as 48 km (30 miles) an hour.

THINKING SERIOUSLY ABOUT PIG KEEPING?

Although pigs are truly delightful creatures, not everyone in the world is in love with them. Pigs are really very clean, despite protestations to the contrary from their detractors. But a large number of pigs will create a certain amount of noise and odours, so if you are thinking 'several' or 'a lot' you should also think carefully about where you are going to situate them. This means away from residential houses; either on a farm or on a reasonably isolated country property.

On the other hand, you will need good access to your pigs for a variety of reasons:
- You will need to feed your pigs and inspect them regularly.
- If you have an ill pig or a sow giving birth.
- For the convenience of pig feed deliveries.

You may need planning permission to erect permanent buildings or extend existing ones, particularly if you have a private house or a smallholding. A larger farm, on the other hand, may not need to do so. If in doubt, you should contact your local planning authority. It's usually a good idea to tell your nearest neighbours as well; you don't want them finding out first by seeing a planning permission application stuck to a tree outside your door.

REGISTERING PIGS, SHEEP AND GOATS

Whether you keep one animal as a pet or a commercial herd/flock you need to be registered with Defra (Department for Environment, Food and

Rural Affairs). If you already keep sheep, goats or pigs and have not registered them, you must do so immediately.

Before moving livestock to your holding, you need a County Parish Holding (CPH) number for the land where the livestock will be kept. The CPH is a nine digit number; the first two digits relate to the county, the next three relate to the parish and the last four digits are a unique number to the keeper, e.g. 12/345/6789. To apply for a CPH you need to contact the Rural Payments Agency (RPA) on 0845 6037777.

Once you have your CPH you can move the livestock to your holding under a General Licence. The next step is to register your livestock with Defra. You need to contact your local Animal Health Divisional Office (AHDO). www.defra.gov.uk/animalhealth

You will be asked for your CPH as a reference and will be able to register your livestock over the phone. If your correspondence address is different from the herd/flock location, inform the AHDO and confirm they have the correct details.

When your livestock are registered, a flock/herd mark will automatically be created. Herdmarks for pigs are one or two letters followed by four digits, e.g. AB1234 or A1234. Flock/herd marks for sheep and goats are six digits only. The Defra herdmark provides a quick and effective means of identifying premises from which livestock have moved. It is unique, kept on a single database and available to inspectors for rapid tracing. The AHDO will send you a registration document, which will contain your personal details, CPH and flock/herd mark. You will also receive a booklet, *The Welfare of Pigs and Pig Identification*. If any of your details change, you must tell your AHDO within one month of the change.

If pigs need to be moved, they require a movement licence to travel with them. Again, there is more information about this on the Defra website.

Once the pigs are on your land, they may not be moved for 20 days. This is to protect against the spread of any outbreak of disease.

It is recommended that all prospective pigkeepers read the booklet *Code of Recommendations for the Welfare of Livestock: Pigs* published by Defra. It is available online www.defra.gov.uk, by email: defra@iforcegroup.com or free of charge from Defra Publications, Admail 6000, London SW1A 2XX or by telephone order: 0845 955 6000.

Defra has also published a really useful document called *A Guide for New Keepers — Pigs* with loads of information and useful addresses and telephone numbers. www.defra.gov.uk/animalh/id-move/pigs/pdf/new_owner_guide.pdf that can be downloaded from the internet, or you can call the Defra Livestock Identification helpline at 0845 050 9876 to request it.

It is also a good idea to have a chat with a local veterinary surgeon to find out if they have any experience with farm animals, and if not if there is someone they can refer you to to look after the health of your pigs.

All this red tape and forms may have already put you off, but if you think about these rules as protection for you and your prospective pigs, rather than pointless bureaucracy, it might not seem quite so onerous.

The biggest problem in my opinion is becoming too involved, if that's the right word. Keeping animals — pigs, goats, chickens, whatever, can be very addictive. About five years ago, the alpaca farm down the road from where I live started out by wanting to buy one pig. The farmers came home with the pig, plus three goats! They now breed kune kune and pygmy pigs, chickens, ducks, quail, goats, alpacas, Akita dogs and soay sheep and probably other animals I haven't seen yet, all bred for pets. Some of the animals have been rescued and the livestock at least all seem to have names.

If you are still reading, you probably have enough commitment to go ahead and take the plunge.

A GOOD PLACE TO START

A sensible way to start keeping pigs either as pets or future food, is to take a pig keeping course.

Many breeders provide one-day courses and 'piggy weekends', which offer hands-on advice to those who are smallholders new to pig keeping, or those who are just thinking about keeping pigs.

These courses usually offer the following content:

- Looking at the various breeds and their suitability for your needs
- What you should look for when buying your first pig
- Legislation you need to know about
- Records you need to keep
- Who to contact for advice and help
- General health overview, including worming, injections and basic first aid
- Housing, fencing and equipment
- Feeding and handling
- Breeding
- Other benefits of keeping pigs
- Taking your pigs to slaughter
- How to produce outstanding quality pork (if this is your interest in pig keeping)
- How to be cost-effective and save money if you are keeping your pig as a pet.

Since these courses are usually tailored to either specific breeds, keeping pigs as pets or pig keeping for pork production, you will want to do some research before you sign up. I have listed some possible venues:

Pig Paradise Farm www.pigparadise.com

Barton Hill Kune Kune Pigs www.bartonhill.co.uk

Bidgiemire Pig Co. www.pig-arcs.co.uk

Oaklands Pigs www.oaklandspigs.co.uk

Empire Farm www.empirefarm.co.uk

Yearle Tamworths www.yearletamworths.co.uk

Pig in a Day
www.rivercottage.net/ShopProduct22/PiginaDay.aspx

You will find others in magazines, on the internet, through breeders, or by word of mouth from friends.

WHICH BREED OF PIG IS FOR ME?

MODERN MEAT BREEDS

A distinction of sorts is now made between coloured and white breeds of pigs. Although all of today's pigs are selectively bred for leanness, efficiency and meatier carcasses, the coloured breeds are still considered to have superior 'economic' traits. As a group they are noted for their vigour, faster, yet leaner growth and higher ratio of meat over fat.

On the other hand, the white breeds (white breeds aren't really white — they are a sort of pink or very, very pale beige), are strong in the traits needed for successful pig farming. They milk better than the current breeds and tend to farrow larger litters. They also have the docile nature needed when you are raising and weaning large litters. On commercial farms the goal is to blend the genetic traits of coloured and white pigs to produce a large number of pigs possessing the best qualities of each.

There are 13 traditional pig breeds in the UK today:

Berkshire

During the 17th century, when Cromwell's troops were quartered in Reading during the Civil War, reference was made to a locally-bred pig renowned for its size and the quality of its bacon and ham. This was one of the earliest records of the Berkshire breed.

Cromwell's Berkshires were larger and coarser than our current breed and their colour varied from black to sandy red; sometimes they were spotted and had white patches.

The introduction of Chinese and Siamese blood resulted in the development of the Berkshires we are familiar with today — a smaller animal, black in colour with rather short, upright (prick) ears, white socks and splashes of white found predominantly in the face and lower half of the body.

At one time the Berkshire had a very short and upturned snout, but selective breeding in recent years has removed this trait, which many people thought was conducive to respiratory problems and feed waste.

The Berkshire suffered a serious decline in popularity after World War II, when the demand for leaner bacon from white-skinned pigs increased, and then again in the 1960s when white breeds were once more favoured by breeders.

In spite of this, the Berkshire survived and our increasing interest in traditional meat has renewed the appeal of this breed. The Berkshire is a traditional pork pig that produces some mouthwatering joints and chops with 'crackling' that is second to none. The excellent carcass quality made it an early favourite with the Royal Family who for years kept a large Berkshire herd at Windsor Castle. The first Berkshire pig ever recorded was the boar 'Ace of Spades' bred by Queen Victoria.

Although it is a coloured breed, the meat dresses out white, and it is noted for its exceptional table qualities. This UK breed is in great demand overseas, especially in Japan, where it is marketed as 'Black Pork' at a premium price because the Japanese believe it has an exceptional flavour.

British Landrace

The first Landrace pigs were imported into Britain from Sweden in 1949 (four boars and eight gilts) with other imports to follow from 1953 onwards. These came into Northern Ireland, the Isle of Man and the Channel Islands.

They are the longest of all the popular breeds and are also known for their distinctive drooping ears. The British Landrace is a very versatile breed, performing well under either indoor or outdoor systems of management. Sows have the ability to produce and rear large litters of piglets with very good daily gain and high lean meat content, in a superbly fleshed carcass, which is ideal for either fresh pork or bacon production. The greatest strength of the Landrace is its undisputed ability to improve other breeds of pig when crossed to produce hybrid gilts: over 90% of hybrid gilt production in Western Europe and North America uses Landrace bloodlines as the foundation for the profitable production of quality pig meat.

British Saddleback

The British Saddleback is an amalgamation of two breeds that shared a similar colour pattern — the

Essex and the Wessex Saddleback. Both date back to 1918.

The Essex pig, mostly found in East Anglia, had a black head and neck and a belt of white over the shoulders and forelegs. The rest of the body was black with the exception of its white feet and the tip of its tail.

The Wessex originated in the New Forest as a cross between two old English bacon pigs. It was black all over except for a continuous belt of white hair over the shoulders and forelegs.

The British Saddleback breed was established in 1967. Saddlebacks are hardy and noted for their mothering qualities and grazing abilities.

Gloucestershire Old Spot

Perhaps Britain's favourite pig, Gloucestershire Old Spots have only had pedigree status since the early 20th century although, if we look at old paintings, they have been depicted on canvas for at least two or three centuries. They are the oldest pedigree spotted pigs in the world.

GOSs are the traditional breed from the apple orchards of Gloucestershire and were raised mainly as domestic animals. They are easily distinguished by the large black spots on their backs and soft, floppy ears. Local folklore has it that the spots are the result of apples falling onto them as they foraged for food. It is very much a smallholder's pig and was known in its early days as the 'Orchard' pig. Lop-eared and a good mother, its attraction to first time pig keepers can be well understood.

Old Spots are ideally suited to an outdoor life; provided they have a warm and comfortable house to go to, they will thrive outside all year round, preferably on land that is reasonably dry so that it does not become a quagmire. They are big pigs and said to be good grazers. The sows are known for their large litters and high milk production.

It was a seriously endangered breed until the end of the 20th century when its numbers increased as a result of the development of a speciality market by the Rare Breeds Survival Trust for its pork and bacon. Because of the difficulties of selling spotted and coloured pigs to butchers (it was harder work to clean them and they claimed that customers did not want such pigs), there was a tendency to breed pigs with as few spots as possible.

The Old Spot is a wonderful pig that owes much of its success and survival to George Styles, who in some circles is affectionately known as the 'Grandfather of the Breed'. Thanks to his passion and interest the breed survived and flourished at a time when without such support we might have found ourselves with far fewer bloodlines.
The GOS produces top quality chops, roasts and sausages. It is often featured in restaurant menus and many butchers now specialise in it.

Hampshire
The Hampshire originated in Britain, was developed

in the US from stock imported from Wessex in 1832 (the date recorded in the 'Hampshire Blue Book' published in 1928) and brought back to the UK in 1968. It is said to now be one of the world's most important breeds.

The Hampshire is a black pig with a distinctive white belt encircling its shoulders and forelegs, quite like the Saddleback. With erect ears and a trim appearance, the Hampshire is very alert and vibrant. Many keepers favour pigs with erect ears, believing them to be easier to handle.

Large Black
With its large lop ears and long, deep body, the Large Black (often called Cornish Black) is Britain's only all-black pig. It is also known as the 'elephant pig' because of the similarity the newly born piglets have to a very small black elephant. Viewed from behind, after just being born, their huge ears and little straight tail certainly make one think of a baby elephant.

Extremely docile and very hardy, it is ideally suited to simple outdoor living. These characteristics, coupled with its black skin, make the Large Black ideal for a wide range of climatic conditions. In fact, by 1935, pigs of this breed had been exported to well over 30 countries.

The breed originates from the Old English Hog established in the 16th and 17th centuries. By the late 1880s there were two distinct types of Large Black, one to be found in East Anglia and the other in Devon and Cornwall. In the early part of the 20th century, Large Blacks were widely distributed throughout the country and were frequently crossed with Large Whites and Middle Whites to produce bacon and pork pigs. The Large Black breed was also very successful in the show ring at this time; at Smithfield in 1919, the Supreme Championship was awarded to a Large Black sow, which subsequently sold for 700 guineas. The same year the breed outnumbered all other breeds at the Royal Show when 121 Large Black pigs were exhibited.

A change in demand by the meat trade and a developing prejudice against coloured pigs led to a severe decline in numbers throughout the 1960s. Today, Large Blacks can be found throughout the British Isles, mainly in small herds, some of which were established well before World War II. Despite its size it is both docile and an excellent mother, capable of rearing large litters and producing excellent bacon for the table.

Current demand for meat produced from traditional breeds of pigs is now promoting a growth in the number of breeders keeping Large Blacks, as this particular breed is much appreciated for its succulent taste and eating quality. The Large Black is really much more of a bacon pig than the smaller, rounder and much chunkier pork pigs.

This is, without any doubt, one of the more graceful, elegant members of the pig family.

Large White

Large Whites are distinguished by their erect ears and slightly dished faces (which means the faces are longer than other pigs and the eyes are set back farther than other breeds). They are long-bodied with excellent hams and fine white hair and, as their name suggests, they are characterised by their large size.

The early history of this breed in Yorkshire is difficult to trace. The large, coarse-boned and leggy white pigs of the region were crossed with other breeds. It has been suggested that among these were the Cumberland, Leicestershire and the Middle and Small White. Specimens of the new breed first attracted attention at the Windsor Royal Show in 1831. The stock used in the development and improvement of the pigs in that area is not as important as what was finally produced as a breed.

Before the end of the 19th century, British Large Whites were already establishing themselves all over the world. Innovative pedigree breeders were exporting breeding stock as far afield as Australia, Argentina, Canada and Russia as well as most countries in Europe.

The Large White has proved itself as a rugged and hardy breed that can withstand variations in climate and other environmental factors. Their ability to cross with and improve other breeds has given them a leading role in commercial pig production systems around the world.

Mangalitza/Lincolnshire Curly Coated

Is it a pig or a sheep? The Lincolnshire Curly Coated was the only British pig that had to be sheared and whose hair was woven/knitted to produce an attractive series of men's sweaters. This extinct, yet much-missed pig was a giant, sometimes weighing over 250 kg (550 lb/39 st). It was more fat than lean and had powerful shoulders higher than a person's waist. And it was very, very hairy.

Although sadly the Lincolnshire Curly Coated breed died out in Britain in 1972, the breed had been exported to Austria and Hungary early in the 20th century because it was a successful and hardy stock, capable of withstanding their harsh winters. The Hungarians crossed the Lincoln with their Mangalitza (a similar curly-coated pig). Thankfully, though, after 10 years and much red tape, Tony York (Pig Paradise) has imported all three Mangalitza breed lines to the UK (the 'Blonde', 'Swallow Bellied' and the 'Red'). An account can be found on his website, along with pictures of several of the pigs.
www.pigparadise.com/curly.html

There are now more than 48 Mangalitzas in the UK. They might be Austro-Hungarian in origin, rather than English, but they do offer a glimpse of our lost farming heritage and one of our more uncommon domestic farm breeds. Recent births have attracted considerable media interest (usually under 'Is it a sheep or a pig?'). The Mangalitza is not acknowledged by the Rare Breed Survival Trust as a Lincolnshire Curly Coated because the Trust feels they should be recognised in their own right.

Middle White

So ugly that it is beautiful, the Middle White is a magnificent pig with a flattened face and nose and big pricked ears with a feathering of hairs around the edges. When it comes towards you, it looks like a vampire bat!

The Middle White was first recognised as a breed in 1852 in most unusual circumstances. At the Keighley Agricultural Show in West Yorkshire, Joseph Tuley, a weaver by trade, exhibited several of his famous Large White sows along with other pigs.

The judges could not agree, as some of the animals were not considered sufficiently large for the class, and as the merits of these pigs were so extraordinary, entirely forbidding recourse to disqualification, a committee was summoned. The judges declared that, if removed from the Large White class, the pigs would not be eligible for the Small White class, so it was decided to provide a third class and to call it the 'Middle Breed'.

The Small White had been developed for showing, and derived from crossing the local pigs with imported Chinese and Siamese pigs from which it inherited the dished face, and so much the characteristic of the Middle White. In further establishing the Middle White breed, Tuley took a second cross with a boar of the Small White breed and females from the best type of Large White in his herd. The resulting progeny were as heavy as the pure Large White, although in type and lightness of offal and head they much resembled the best of the Small White breed. The Small White breed became extinct in 1912. Due to the 'new' breed's eating qualities, its early maturing and its very easy management, the Middle White went from strength to strength.

When the National Pig Breeders Association was founded in 1884, the Middle White along with the Large White and Tamworth were the three foundation breeds and their first Herd books were published that same year. The Middle White remained very popular with butchers everywhere, particularly in London where the breed was known as 'the London Porker', as the carcasses could be cut into the small joints favoured in the first part of 20th century. World War II and meat rationing until 1954 led to a concentration on the 'bacon' pig and the specialist pork pig was sidelined.

Along with other pork breeds the quantity of Middle Whites declined sharply during this period. Fortunately, a number of dedicated breeders ensured the continuation of the breed. In recent years the demand for meat with good eating qualities has once again led to Middle White pork appearing on the menus of top London restaurants, with glowing reports regarding its outstanding quality. Middle White breeding stock has been exported worldwide, and the breed is particularly appreciated in Japan, where it is known as 'Middle York'. The Middle White has many assets: it is very easily managed; it is docile and can make a contribution to crossbreeding programmes to improve eating quality.

The Middle White Pig Breeders Club established in 1990 has as its patron the well-known chef Antony Worrall Thompson whose enthusiasm has led him to breed his own Middle White pigs.

Oxford Sandy and Black

The Oxford Sandy and Black Pig is sometimes referred to as a 'Plum Pudding Pig' (because it looks a bit like a Christmas pudding in colour) or an 'Oxford Forest Pig'.

It is one of the oldest British pig breeds, having existed for 200—300 years — a traditional farmer's and cottager's pig, of the middle part of the country, especially around Oxfordshire.

It seems to be closely linked to the old Berkshire and Tamworth. But it is not known whether it diverged from them or was the result of crossbreeding, or crossbreeding with an entirely different breed — no one is entirely certain.

The Oxford Sandy and Black reached crisis point at least twice in its past when numbers dropped so low that extinction was a real possibility. Except for a few dedicated breeders, the OSB would surely have been lost. In 1973 the Rare Breeds Survival Trust was formed giving hope for the breed, but the Trust decided not to recognise it.

Sadly some of the bloodlines have been lost, but today's enthusiastic breeders are determined to save the remaining lines. The current picture is very encouraging with the rarest bloodlines hanging on and slowly increasing. Hopefully the breed is at last safe (although still relatively few in number).

The breed has many good qualities, especially its excellent temperament and mothering abilities. Prolific and hardy, it is particularly suited to outdoor life, being a good forager and as it is a coloured pig with a good coat, it is far less prone to sunburn.

In any litter the piglets can range from all sand (resembling a Tamworth) to white or pale cream with black spots (looking like a Gloucester Old Spot). They are occasionally almost black (very similar to a Berkshire). While having such a variety of colours makes the litter very attractive, the only pigs that can be registered are those that meet the following breed standards:

Sandy (dark to light) with black blotches (not spots). Ears must be lop or semi lop. 'Prick' ears are not acceptable. Underline (number of teats) must be minimum 12 for a gilt or 14 for a boar. White tip to tail, four white feet and a white blaze is an added bonus.

This breed is renowned for the quality of pork and bacon that it produces and as colour doesn't matter when it comes to rearing for meat, there is always an outlet for unrecognised pigs.

This is one of the best pigs for a first time pig keeper. It has a great personality, is very docile, is a wonderful mother and is easy to handle. This pig does not seem to have any undesirable qualities and is very good with children.

Pietrain
Pietrain, Belgium, the village from which the breed takes its name, was the birthplace of the breed. Belgium has a reputation for breeding animals with high meat to bone ratio, thus providing high yield profitable carcasses. The pig breeding industry in Belgium is no exception to the sourcing of new genetics in this way and in the 1920s Gloucester Old Spots were brought from the UK to improve the local breeds. These boars were crossed with local sows, and slowly but surely the Pietrain breed was established.

The breed was officially recognised in 1956 following the attention it attracted at that time during a severe depression in the pig market. Certain boars were noted for their ability to sire litters with high conformation hindquarters and lean loins. From then on, the breed has benefited from its particular genetic characteristics.

Pig farmers in the UK will tell you that a Pietrain is stress-positive and tends to die at the slightest excuse, but this is not the case any longer as it has been bred out.

The breed is of medium size and is white with black spots. Around the black spots there are characteristic rings of light pigmentation that carry white hair. This, coupled with the fact that the black hair is not as deeply pigmented as on black breeds, or the black spots on some spotted breeds, leaves them with rather unattractive coats. The breed is commonly referred to as being of piebald markings. The ears are carried erect.

The Pietrain is quite distinct. It is shorter of leg than most breeds, stockier in build and quite broad along the back. The hams are extremely bulging and muscular and carry a very high proportion of lean to fat.

The Pietrain has developed a reputation for improving the quality of market swine when the boars are mated with sows of other breeds. While the Pietrain has recently been losing popularity in its native country, it does have the potential to provide genetic improvement in carcass quality. This is what its role seems to be in the UK.

Tamworth

The Tamworth breed is red or ginger, and descends from the Old English Forest Pig. Regarded by many as the aristocrat of the pig world, this magnificently long legged ginger pig with wonderful large pricked up ears will always command attention.

Although in its present form the Tamworth as we know it today is a very distinctive pig with its long legs, prick ears and a pure red or ginger coat, this has not always been the case. Around 1800 it was said to be much smaller with shorter legs and ears that were far less prominent. As far as colour was concerned, it was described as spotted red and brown.

Old pictures of the Tamworth show it to have been anything from white or pale ginger with black spots to a red and black pig. It looked like a picture painted of an old Berkshire and closely resembled the current requirements of the Oxford Sandy and Black.

The Tamworth is one of the great 'dual purpose' pigs, producing stunningly good pork as well as equally tremendous bacon. In the mid 1990s, the Tamworth came top in a taste test carried out by Bristol University using both commercial and rare breed pigs in a scientifically controlled experiment. It was later suggested that further investigation should take place to establish just what it was that gave the Tamworth meat such a distinctive taste, putting it way above all the other breeds.

Although sometimes referred to as 'boisterous', this should not be interpreted as being 'nasty' or difficult to handle. The Tamworth is a large pig that is full of life — an affectionate, talkative pig that is really a gentle giant.

One of the longest snouted pigs, it is of great use to the organic gardener or anyone who has a piece of rough, overgrown land that needs clearing. The Tamworth could certainly earn its keep as a professional rotary tiller!

Tamworths originated near Tamworth, Staffordshire. It has been less affected by Asian strains than other breeds in the UK; its long snout is typical of old British stock; the prick-eared

Tamworth is active and suited to outdoor living, being used in woodland and scrub reclamation projects where its colour protects it from sunburn (very unlike its human ginger counterparts!).

Two Tamworth pigs were running around the town where I live in 1998, having escaped from a local abbatoir. You can read about their adventures on page 148.

Welsh

The earliest references to a Welsh pig come from the 1870s, when there was a considerable trade in Welsh and Shropshire pigs into Cheshire for fattening on milk by-products. Increased demand for pork and bacon during World War I led to the creation of the first pig breed society in Wales in 1918.

The Welsh pig is white, with lop ears meeting at the tips just short of the pig's nose. It has a long body with deep strong hams and legs set well apart. George Eglington, acknowledged as the founder of the modern Welsh breed, described the perfect Welsh pig as 'pear shaped' when viewed from either the side or from above. They are still known for their hardiness and ability to thrive under a wide variety of conditions, both indoors and outside.

Since the 1980s the number of registrations has declined, but the breed continues to play a valuable role in crossbreeding programmes.

The Welsh breed is currently on the Rare Breeds Trust watchlist as Category 3, Vulnerable.

RARE PIG BREEDS

The native pig of the British Isles was a large, rangy, lop-eared animal that was kept in pannage (acorns and beechnuts used as forage for woodland pigs), or later in the backyard sty of rural cottages.

In the late 18th century there was an influx of small, fat, prick-eared pigs of Asian origin. The mingling of these two types formed the basis for the creation of all the native British breeds and these were the dominant breeds until the second half of the 20th century.

Although at this time numbers for the Wessex and Essex breeds (now combined as British Saddleback) and the Large Black were still reasonably healthy, others such as the Berkshire, Middle White and Tamworth numbers showed a considerable decline. This was probably due to demand for a different type of pig for bacon, and the recommendation of the Howitt report to the government in 1955, that British pig farming should focus on just three breeds of pig: Large White, Landrace and Welsh.

Native pig breeds that became extinct include the Cumberland, Lincolnshire Curly Coated, Ulster White, Dorset Gold Tip and Yorkshire Blue. They possessed special and distinctive characteristics, which are now no longer available to us. Those native breeds, which have survived, are demonstrating their qualities already as new factors exerting an influence in the marketplace. Increasing awareness of the importance of traditional values is focusing attention on the conservation of native breeds, while the non-intensive systems of management under which these breeds thrive are compatible with the standards of animal welfare, human health and protection of the environment that modern society demands.

Pig breeds are particularly susceptible to changes in the economic climate, and the population of individual breeds can fluctuate dramatically. The cost of feed and the selling price of breeding or finished stock are the main factors affecting the viability of a pig enterprise. Disease can also have a significant impact. Although specific pig diseases such as Swine Fever and Aujesky's have now been eradicated from mainland Britain, other diseases, such as FMD (Foot and Mouth Disease) with the possibility of widespread culling, remain a threat to all our rare and native species.

The Rare Breeds Survival Trust publishes a 'Watchlist' of breeds that are in danger of dying out. For pigs, calculated from data supplied by the British Pig Association — Category 1 (Critical) is <100 registered breeding females, Category 2 (Endangered) 200, Category 3 (Vulnerable) 300, Category 4 (At Risk) 500, Category 5 (Minority) 1000 and Category 6 (Other Native Breeds) is >1000.

At the beginning of 2008, the following breeds were classified as endangered: British Lop and Middle White; Berkshire, Large Black, Tamworth and Welsh were classified as vulnerable; British Saddleback was considered at risk and Gloucestershire Old Spot was called minority.

KUNE KUNE

Kune Kune (pronounced Cooney Cooney, meaning fat and round in Maori) are small pigs from New Zealand. There are no indigenous land animals in New Zealand so there is a bit of mystery about how they got there. There are many theories: the Maoris may have taken them, as the pig was very important to the Polynesians and there are still pigs with tassels in the South Pacific Islands; early whalers and sealers may have taken them, to be released to breed or to be culled for food on their next voyage; or they could have been brought by the people who settled to farm in the country since all farm stock was imported. They may also be a mixture of pigs from many sources, but whatever their origins they have evolved into a charming little pig.

In New Zealand Kunes came very close to extinction in the 1970s. They were not used much for meat anymore by the Maoris and were virtually unknown to the rest of the population. It was then that two wildlife park owners, Michael Willis and John Simster, heard about this pig and set out across New Zealand to buy every Kune they could find for sale. This only amounted to 18 pigs, and from this original stock, with later additions of more animals, the Kune population in New Zealand is now in a healthy state and is in great demand as a smallholder's pig.

Kune Kunes arrived in Britain in 1992. Zoe Lindop and Andrew Calveley had worked in New Zealand for several years and were charmed by the Kune Kune. After meeting Michael Willis and learning how endangered these little pigs were, they decided to import a small group to breed in Britain. As the Kunes only existed in New Zealand it was important to build a population in another country, in case of disease in their homeland. Michael bred a wide range of Kunes because it was vital to have as wide a variation of genetic stock brought into the UK as possible. If they had only brought one type, we would not be preserving a true representation of the breed.

Kune Kunes look like Walt Disney cartoon versions of a pig. They are between 61–76 cm (24–30 inches) high, and 54.5–109 kg (120–240 lb/8½–17 st) in weight. They are completely covered in hair, which can be anything between short and straight, and long and curly. They come in a range of colours — cream, ginger, brown, black and spotted. They have a medium to short snout, and either prick or flopped ears. They have short legs and a short round body. The most unusual feature of most Kune Kune pigs is a pair of tassels called *piri piri* under their chin like a goat. This is not unique to the Kunes, but it is unusual. Temperament-wise, they are delightful, being placid and very friendly. They thrive on human company, therefore making excellent pets.

The Kune Kune is a breed that shows a lot of genetic variation. This is one of their charms, and most people find they have favourite types of kunes and breed accordingly. The Maoris preferred black pigs, but in the UK spotted pigs seem in favour at the moment. We must be careful and breed all types and colours of Kunes. To help a rare breed you must preserve as much of the gene pool as possible and not breed for fads and fashion, which inevitably leads to changing the breed forever. In Britain we have adopted the New Zealand standard of perfection for Kunes: this standard concentrates on correct conformation and good temperament.

In 1993 Zoe imported a further two bloodlines and in 1996 Andy Case imported three more bloodlines into the UK. Kune Kune pigs are now becoming established in Britain, with about 600 purebred registered pigs.

VIETNAMESE POTBELLIED

Vietnamese Potbellied pigs are a dwarf pig breed that was developed in Vietnam in the 1960s. Considerably smaller than standard American or European farm pigs, most adult potbellied pigs are about the size of a medium- or large-breed dog, although they are much heavier. They were brought into Sweden and Canada and have since moved into a number of different countries.

When Canadian Keith Connell imported the first potbellied pigs into North America, he had no idea what he had started. Originally, he intended to supply the pigs to zoos, but a private buyer interested in the pigs as pets started the porcine pets on their way to worldwide distribution and fame. In 1986, when the first potbellies were sold into the US, their market price ran well into the thousands of dollars. Recently, as breeders caught up with the market demand, the price of pigs has come down to match that of pedigreed dogs and cats, making them an affordable alternative.

The original Canadian pigs averaged 114 kg (250 lb/ 18 st) and were, therefore, miniature pigs when compared to domestic swine that weigh 273–682 kg (600–1500 lb/43–107 st). Full-grown potbellied pigs weigh an average of 31.8–68.2 kg (70–150 lb/5– 10.7 st) with some reaching 91 kg (200 lb/14.3 st) or more; they average almost 1 metre (3 ft) long and 37.5 cm (15 inches) tall. Full growth is not reached until they are about 5 years old. Colours range from solid black to solid white, with a variety of spots in between. People ask, 'Which make better pets: males or females?' We have found that as long as either sex is neutered or spayed, it really doesn't matter. Unspayed females suffer from PMS and strong mood swings; intact males produce a pungent odour in addition to displaying other unpleasant traits — neither are desirable pets. A neutered male is called a 'barrow', an intact male is a 'boar', a female that has never had babies is called a 'gilt' and a female that has given birth is a 'sow'.

Most people who purchase these pigs want them as pets, but they do not necessarily stay small, cute, or cuddly. As stated above, their average weight is close to 45.5 kg (100 lb/7 st), and they do not like to be picked up or held. Unlike cats and dogs, pigs are prey not predators, so being lifted up or restrained causes them extreme alarm. In this respect they are comparable to ferrets as pets. Therefore, attempts by humans at lifting or hugging are always interpreted by the pig as hostile and result in struggling and squealing. The one time pigs will welcome close contact is to huddle while sleeping, an instinct which conserves body heat and provides protection. Human owners usually have to settle for acceptance of affectionate contact when the animals sleep. This quirk makes potbellied pigs less than ideal pets for children, who usually insist on showing their affection through hugging and handling.

So do these potbellied pigs make good pets? The short answer is no. Pigs really need to be outside where they can root and cool themselves down and interact with other pigs. Some breeders will tell you that Potbellied pigs can be kept in a flat, but this is quite irresponsible and untrue.

Potbellied pigs require good maintenance. If this doesn't happen it could be harmful to both the pig and the owner. Male Potbellies grow tusks which need to be trimmed, but not removed. Their hooves also need to be trimmed about once a year, which is probably best done under sedation by a vet. Potbellied pigs shed once or twice a year and should be brushed to keep their hair and skin healthy. The lighter-coloured ones also are prone to sunburn, so sun creams are necessary if they will be outside in the hot sun. Having a pig as a house pet requires some preparation: pig proofing the house as one would for a toddler is a must.
But some owners have had positive experiences with their Potbellies. Pigs are highly intelligent animals and easy to train to perform tricks for a food treat reward. Many pig owners walk their pets on leads using a harness.

George Clooney, the actor, owned a Vietnamese Potbellied pig named Max for almost 19 years. When he first purchased Max as a cute little piglet, nobody told him that one day the pig would weigh over 136 kg (300 lb/21½ st). But George loved Max even when he got to be a big bruiser, telling people that this was the longest relationship he ever had! Max died an old man at 19 in 2006.

If you are thinking of adopting or buying a Vietnamese Potbellied pig, you need to arm yourself with all the information you can. The internet contains a lot of facts about their pros and cons, but talking to a knowledgeable breeder or owner is probably your best bet.

MINI PIGS ARE A HUGE SUCCESS

In 2007 the BBC news channel told the story of Pennywell Farm in Devon: a fun farm that was breeding miniature pigs. These pigs, a variant of the Kune Kune, are about one-fifth the size of an ordinary pig and have been a big success with visitors.

Chris Murray, co-owner of the farm, began cross-breeding the pigs nine years ago and believes he now has the perfect pig. He says that most pigs are very cute when they are young, but they outgrow a home environment and can be aggressive when they get older. These miniatures are happy either indoors or outdoors.

Some pet pigs, such as the Vietnamese Potbelly, have in the past been bought for their 'cuteness', but they fell out of fashion once it became clear how large they grew.

The Pennywell miniatures are easy to house train and have a good temperament. Normally if you pick up one of the baby pigs in a litter, the sow would snap at you, but these mums are amazingly content.

According to the BBC report, the world's smallest pig seems to be the 71 cm (28-inch) wild pygmy hog: an endangered species living in wildlife sanctuaries in Assam, India.

EVERYTHING YOU NEED TO KNOW

BUYING YOUR PIGS

I am assuming that you are not going into large-scale pig keeping, but only planning to raise a couple or few, either as pets, or to eventually provide food for the table in humane, non-intensive circumstances.

Whether you are going the pet route or table route, you will probably choose one of the traditional breeds. Not only will this pursuit bring you lots of pleasure, but it will help to keep our endangered species from dying out.

Remember though, that an ordinary cute little eight-week-old piglet will weigh about 114 kg (250 lb/18 st) at six months of age. So try to be practical and if you haven't got enough space to keep an animal of this size; either think about one of the mini pigs or choose another animal.

As with poultry, you should buy from a reputable breeder. You should consider the breed characteristics and how these fit in with your requirements and abilities. Some breeds, such as Berkshire or Large Black, are more placid and easy to manage, while others, such as the Tamworth, are boisterous and lively and bound to find ways of escaping. Two very enterprising Tamworth pigs did just that (see page 148). Kune Kunes are smaller, very friendly and good as pets. Once you've decided what breed you want, contact the breed society for help. Full details of rare breed societies can be found on the Rare Breeds Survival Trust website.

Country Smallholding and similar magazines will have 'pigs for sale' classified adverts.

You can either choose a registered pedigreed pig or a crossbred pig. A pedigreed pig must be registered as part of a litter before it is 10 weeks old — it cannot be individually registered afterwards. This may only be important if you plan to breed the pig or market it. If you are uncertain as to your future plans, though, the piglet(s) should be birth notified and earmarked (notched, tattooed or tagged) just in case.

WHAT TO LOOK FOR IN A HEALTHY PIGLET

Look for a weaner that has a shiny coat and skin that is free from redness or flakiness. The pig should look alert, have bright eyes and come to you when called. Also look at the piglet's current surroundings. Don't buy from a pen where there is any loose manure or if the piglets' tails are wet or dirty. The feet should be strong and level with no signs of a limp, the ears should be clean and warm and the nose should be moist and cold, but not runny.

TRANSPORTING YOUR PIGS
(Bringing home the bacon)

If you have bought a weaner or two, transporting them home is pretty straightforward. A robust cardboard box lined with newspaper and straw is quite sufficient, as is a dog or cat carrier.

To alleviate stress and injury to your pigs, ensure that the carrier is firmly fixed in your vehicle and cannot move or roll around.

Do not feed the pigs until you reach home as little pigs, in particular, are prone to car sickness and this is not the best way to start your relationship with them.

If you have purchased larger pigs, they must be transported in a trailer. By law the trailer must be clean and must be cleaned again within a 24-hour period afterwards. A good pig breeder will know how to best move his pigs; bribery with apples or carrots usually works. Pigs can be very stubborn, and because they are so heavy it is impossible to force them to do anything they have no intention of doing.

When you arrive home, put them in a secure house, not just in the paddock, because their first instinct will be to flee. (It's just as well that pigs can't fly).

With respect to piglets, keep them enclosed for a week or so until they get used to their surroundings and the sound of your voice. Decide what names you will call them and speak to them often. They will begin to recognise their names and respond. A little bribery won't go amiss here, either.

I read somewhere that a pig has the intelligence of a three-year-old toddler. While pigs don't speak a human language, they do understand human speech.

HOUSING YOUR PIGS

The first thing to consider when thinking about raising pigs is where you will house them.
A miniature pig that will be a house pet is one thing, but a hefty porker you will raise for meat is something else entirely. Most people who are not pig farmers, but think about pig ownership as a means of providing meat for the family at a moderate cost, will start with one or two 'weaner' pigs.

Pigs need protection from the elements. In warm weather, they need a home that is dry and sheltered from the sun. Pigs only have sweat glands on their snouts and will sunburn and overheat quickly. In the winter they also need a dry home that is protected from the cold, wind and snow.

You must also bear in mind that pigs grow faster than any other farm animal and, with proper feeding, will gain nearly 114 kg (250 lb/18 st) in six months! So you must provide sturdy accommodation that is not too small. You should size the pen to the eventual size of the pigs.

HOW MUCH LAND DO YOU NEED?

The amount of land depends on how you will be rearing your pigs. Free-ranging requires either sufficient woodland or subdivided paddocks so that you can rotate the living space of your animals. This will give the land an opportunity to rest and provide your pigs with a change of environment. *The Code of Recommendations on the Welfare of*

Livestock advises about 5 animals per half acre (.2 hectare). This could be subdivided into two areas of $^1/_2$ acre each (.1 hectare). Each of the subdivisions will nicely house 2–3 pigs, their living quarters and an area they can roam at will.

If you are farming as well, cultivating at least one crop on your land when it is not being used by the pigs will help the ground recover and keep it fertile.

Pigs are pretty good at dealing with various ground conditions, but clay soil is the worst as it gets muddy in wet weather. If you have a choice, sandy soil is your best bet. While concrete is a good surface around pig houses and feeding areas, it can be slippery in wet and icy weather. So when pouring concrete, make sure it is roughed up to make it easier for the pigs to walk in bad climate conditions. Your pigs must also have shelter from the sun in the summer: either from trees, roofs, or similar.

ENCLOSURES

You may keep your pigs outside in the warm weather. Fencing is an important consideration; pigs are very curious creatures by nature and like to explore. Even though they become accustomed to their own territory, they are likely to roam; they may stray and even get lost. They can even cause damage by rooting around other people's gardens or running across the road.

The boundary of your property or the borders of their paddocks must therefore be enclosed by some sort of fencing — either a permanent woven wire fence with a board around the base to discourage digging, or temporary moveable electric fencing if you train your pigs to it. A moveable system has the advantage in that it allows you to use the pigs to clear and work a piece of land. Whatever fencing you choose needs to be very sturdy because pigs tend to scratch themselves against trees and posts, and less substantial fences will just not hold up. Post and rail fencing with pig wire stretched tautly between is a good idea. Since pigs will dig under fences, you can either put barbed wire on the bottom, or if the idea of your pig hurting itself on this doesn't appeal to you, horizontal wooden rails at the top, bottom and centre should do the job. If you have very large pigs, you want to build your fence high enough so they can't climb out; if you have quite small ones, you need to make sure there are no gaps they can crawl through.

WHAT SORT OF HOUSE SHOULD YOU HAVE?

In the fairy tale, *The Three Little Pigs*, one of the pigs built a house of straw, one built a house of sticks and the third built his house with bricks. The first two pigs were eaten by the big, bad wolf, while the third lived happily ever after. The first pig took the easy way out, the second was also quite careless, while the third thought carefully about the best solution. In later versions of this story, the first two pigs don't get eaten, but go to live with their more sensible brother.

This doesn't really have anything to do with what sort of accommodation you should provide for your pigs, except that you should suit it to the situation and the type of pigs you have. Ideally, each paddock used by pigs should contain at least one house, somewhere that is easily accessible to you, and if it is on a hill or slope it should be on the top, rather than the bottom, so that it doesn't flood or become muddy.

Pig Sties

A pig sty is the traditional home for a pig. If you have a farm there may be an old pig sty that you could use. They tend to be built of brick, but they are usually fairly small and low-ceilinged and therefore difficult to clean. One problem with old pig sties is that they may not have easy access to the grazing land that is part of the modern outdoor free-range pig's environment.

Ark

The triangular or semicircular ark is the ideal modern housing for pigs, whether you purchase it or build it yourself. Pig houses need to be warm, dry and airy, and the ark fulfils all of these requirements. Wooden floors are warm and comfortable; concrete is easier to clean, but hard. Alternatively, arks without floors will allow you to move them around the paddock to make use of the land on a rotating basis.

Wooden arks are best. You can also get plastic or metal ones, but they tend to be cold in the winter and hot in the summer.

Another shape of ark is the human house shape — straight sides with a pitched roof. If it is high enough, this will allow you to stand while you are cleaning it, but it may be colder for your pigs in the winter. Whatever the shape, the ark should have at least one door to let the pigs enter and leave (or to shut them in or out), and it can also have a window for more air circulation.

Barns

Barns are spacious and airy, but they can also be draughty. They tend to be quite large, so your pigs might decide to use part of it as a toilet, rather than going outside. On the plus side, if the weather is really awful your pigs will have a comfortable place to stay, rather than be confined in a sty or an ark.

Sheds

Sheds can also be adapted to house pigs if they are large enough (the experts say 180 sq cm/6 sq ft per pig) with a similar-sized run outside.

BEDDING

Would you like to sleep on a cold, hard floor? Neither do pigs. They are weighty animals and if left on hard surfaces, they could rub their coats off, develop sores and get chilled.

Although pigs are basically very clean animals who generally do not soil their beds or homes, their bedding needs to be changed frequently as it will get dusty, flattened and muddy over time, which will make it very uncomfortable and could even cause respiratory problems. You should also disinfect your pig houses routinely with either a liquid or powder disinfectant.

Straw is probably the best and most practical bedding for pigs as long as it is not old and dusty. It is reasonably water-resistant, bulky and comfortable. Some pigs will eat straw if it is very fresh or they are very hungry and this will cause tummy upsets if they ingest too much. Barley or wheat straw are both acceptable materials. If you know a friendly farmer, he can provide small quantities of straw for you and you won't have to worry about storing huge amounts. Straw has another advantage in that you can put some outside your pigs' houses for them to use as a mat for their muddy feet.

FEEDING AND WATERING

Pigs get very stressed by change of environment, being transported and leaving the rest of their litter. Try to alleviate the stress by planning ahead. It is probably preferable to feed them the same rations they received in their previous home for a few weeks, and then mixing in new feeds gradually.

A pig that is well looked after should gain approximately 0.45 kg (1 lb) a day while they are in their growing period. Young, growing pigs need a well-balanced diet that is high in protein, vitamins and minerals. The younger the pig, the higher percentage of protein is required. As it matures, it will require a lesser percentage of protein. Pigs are non-ruminants (they don't chew the cud and also, unlike cattle and goats, they only have one stomach).

Pigs really enjoy their food. But they may tend to overeat, causing them to become too fat. If they don't eat enough they will suffer from malnutrition, so it is important to discover not only what, but how much to feed. And you must suit the feed to the type of pig: for example, Kune Kunes and Vietnamese Potbellied pigs need lower protein levels than traditional pigs or they will gain too much weight and develop joint and foot problems.

In nature, pigs will eat little and often, so you could, if you liked, feed them 3—4 times a day to simulate the way they would eat in the wild. However, this is not usually practical for the small pig keeper, so plan to feed them twice a day — in the morning and afternoon. Pigs like feeding routines, so try to feed them at the same times. If you are late serving their meals, they will certainly let you know as they are very good timekeepers. The only 'equipment' you need to hand-feed your pigs is a bucket and a feeding trough. If you are building it yourself, make sure it is sturdy, otherwise your pigs may end up slinging it all over the paddock. And since the trough should be big enough so that all the pigs can feed at the same time, allow 25–45 cm (12–18 inches) for each pig.

What makes it more difficult is that opinions vary on how much you should feed a pig — taking into account its breed, size and age, how much wild food they consume, how much exercise they get, etc. Here is a rough guide: weaned piglets should be fed approximately 450g (1 lb) pig pellets per day for each month of their age up to four months; after that, 1.8 kg (approximately 4 lb) a day should be enough. The feed should have a fairly high protein level (about 18%). Too much protein can cause diarrhoea (scouring) in which case you should decrease the protein.

Just a note about weaning: the traditional time to wean piglets, including the smaller breeds, is at 8 weeks, when their mothers' milk will be drying up and they will be competing for food with her. It is a good idea to keep the sow and piglets where you intend to keep the weaners to begin with. After a day or two, take the sow far enough away from her babies so that she cannot hear them and they cannot hear her. A clean break, rather than a gradual one, is best.

Unless you are exceedingly adept at mathematics and chemistry, you will choose to feed your pigs commercially formulated feed, which will contain all the nutrients your pig needs.

This list provided by W & H Marriage & Sons Ltd. contains examples of the various types of compound feeds. The 'ash' referred to is the mineral content of the feed.

Supergrower pellets — the ideal first diet for young piglets:

Protein	20%
Oil	5.8%
Fibre	3.9%
Ash	5.6%

Grower cubes (sometimes called grower nuts) — a cereal-based grower/fattener ration to be followed on from Supergrower pellets. This can be fed to pigs up to 90 kg (200 lb/14 st) live weight:

Protein	17.4%
Oil	4.0%
Fibre	6.0%
Ash	5.5%

Sow cubes/meal/rolls — a quality diet for both dry and lactating sows:

Protein	16%
Oil	4.0%
Fibre	5.5%
Ash	5.9%

Potbellied pig — specifically designed for the pet pig to promote and maintain health:

Protein	16%
Oil	3.2%
Fibre	6%
Ash	5.4%

Marriage's also manufactures a range of organic pig feed.

Some farmers say you should feed as much as your pigs can eat in 20 minutes. If it is all gone after a few minutes, try feeding more, and if there is still food left after 30 minutes, remove it and cut down on the next feeding.

You can also produce some of your own feed, but you are unlikely to produce all of the elements that go into a balanced diet, so you should only feed your pigs your own produce as a supplement to the commercial feed.

In the UK it is unlawful to feed farm animals, or any other ruminant animals, pigs or poultry, with meat, or any animal by-product (except for fish meal, which can be mixed into pig feed as long as it comes from an approved source and has been properly processed). It is also illegal to feed pigs catering waste or waste that contains, or has been in contact with, meat or meat products — that means all waste food, including used cooking oil or table scraps that may have been in contact with meat.

This is because following the outbreak of Foot and Mouth Disease (FMD) in 2001, the Government reviewed the practice of swill feeding and banned it. Subsequently, new EU regulations on the disposal of animal by-products were introduced in 2002, and also prohibit the feeding of catering waste and any animal by-product.

The Defra guide for new pig keepers mentioned on page 12 has a table showing current controls on the use of waste food for pigs, and as long as it doesn't originate from any catering establishment, some waste can be fed, particularly cereals and vegetables.

Despite these regulations, pigs are omnivores (meaning that they will eat everything, including flesh), so they may eat the odd rabbit or suchlike.

FOOD SUPPLEMENTS AND TREATS

You can supplement your pigs' food with grass, fruit, vegetables and fodder beet. But watch the quantity of fodder beet because the leaves contain oxalic acid, a gastric irritant. Green potatoes should be avoided for the same reason. Apparently pigs just love pumpkin; this is the major pig feed in China. Pigs seem to like all the vine foods humans do, including squashes of all kinds, melons and tomatoes. If you have woodland, your pigs may find roots and acorns, but try to limit the quantity of acorns because they contain tannic acid, another irritant. If you have orchards, your pigs will find windfalls, but don't let them overdose on these either as too much fruit will give them loose bowels and they may become intoxicated from overripe, fermenting apples.

WATER

It is important that pigs should always have access to an ample supply of fresh drinking water and an automatically refilling system is ideal. *The Code of Recommendations for the Welfare of Livestock* offers a guide to the minimum daily requirements for various weights of pigs. Pigs can die or become very ill if they are deprived of water.

Newly weaned   1–1.5 litres per day
Up to 20 kg (44 lb/3 st)   1.5–2 litres per day
20–40 kg (44-88 lb/3-6 st)   2–5 litres per day
Finishing pigs
Up to 100 kg (220 lb/15.7 st)   5–6 litres per day
Sows and gilts (before, in pig
and after producing a litter)   5–8 litres per day
Sows and gilts (in lactation)   15–30 litres per day
Boars   5–8 litres per day

For the small-scale pig keeper, a livestock trough for water will also suffice if it is cleaned and refilled daily. Smaller pigs should have shallower troughs to prevent the piglets drowning.

HAPPY,
HEALTHY PIGS

On the whole, pigs are very hardy and healthy. Rare breeds and those that are traditionally reared are likely to be healthier than intensively reared pigs because they have more freedom of movement, access to the open air and sunlight (when we are lucky enough to have it); they eat healthy feed, they munch grass and they don't have a lot of stress in their lives, so they are happy. All you have to do is look after them, keeping them comfortable and content. When pigs are given good care, they will usually perform very well without special health measures.

It is, of course, important to have a vet who is used to pigs. When you live in a rural agricultural area as I do, this is not a problem (we have several), but if you live in suburbia, you may have to look around a bit further and perhaps get a recommendation from your normal vet.

You should always have a picture in your mind of what a healthy pig looks like, so you can compare it against one who is either off-colour or ill.

A healthy pig always has a curly tail, although Kune Kunes don't have tightly curled ones. It should have a sleek coat, clear skin and bright eyes; it should be active, alert and aware of its surroundings; it will always come to you at feeding time and show a good appetite.

There are some routines you can perform to maintain your pigs' health, such as worming or vaccination, although if you register as organic, these may not be permissible. You can get all the information you need about organic pig farming from the Advisory Committee on Organic Standards (ACOS) www.defra.gov.uk/FARM/ORGANIC/ standards/acos/index.htm or Organic Farmers and Growers, a leading UK certification body www.organicfarmers.org.uk.

A pig will give you many clues when it isn't feeling well, some of which are poor appetite, gauntness, rough coats, dull eyes, excessive coughing, diarrhoea, inactivity and lameness. If you are worried about one or more of your pigs, there are things you can do prior to calling the vet. Some common diseases are colds and flu, skin problems, mange, lice and worms.

Take its rectal temperature; the normal temperature is 38.6°C–38.8°C (101.5°F–102°F). If your pig has a fever, call a vet immediately. Antibiotics will probably sort it out. If the pig's temperature is sub-normal, this is not a good sign either. Confine it to a small area, pile straw around it and wrap it in blankets to warm it up. Also check for discharges from the nose, mouth, eyes or vagina, a difference in urine colour, loose or unusual bowel movements, vomiting, wounds or bleeding and abnormal lumps. When you call the vet, try and give him or her all the information you can.

One common problem with pigs is stress. Transporting them around, introducing them to strange surroundings and strange pigs can frighten or stress a pig. When it is stressed, it is more susceptible to illness. It may go off its feed and grow more slowly. It is important to minimise stress, especially when you first get your pig home.

Some diseases are notifiable, which means if you suspect signs of the disease you must notify the Defra Divisional Veterinary Manager at your local Animal Health Divisional Office. Notifiable diseases are: Swine Fever, Foot and Mouth Disease (FMD), Swine Vesicular Disease, Aujeszky's Disease and Anthrax.

Some newer disease syndromes have been affecting swine and are being addressed by vets, institutions and the Agriculture and Horticulture Development Board (AHDB). Recommendations for avoiding these include common sense rules such as: limiting pig to pig contact; avoiding stress; maintaining good hygiene and maintaining good nutrition. Research on these diseases is currently being carried out and vaccines are being developed.

PIGS ARE NOT JUST FOR CHRISTMAS

There is nothing cuter than a little piglet, but some people who think it would be great to have a pet pig of their own find out very quickly that they have taken on more than they imagined. The film *Babe* also gave both children and adults the impression that keeping a pig is fun. So quite a lot of people acquired what they thought was going to be a little bundle of cuteness only to find out that the reality was nothing like the dream; which soon became a nightmare for its owners and neighbours; which in turn filtered down to animal welfare officers, councils and rescue centres.

There isn't a lot of information about pig rescue centres in the UK. Animal Rescuers www.animalrescuers.co.uk features Grenville Owen, a pig man near Spalding, Lincolnshire, who runs a pig sanctuary for unwanted and abused Potbellied pigs. He is keen to re-home some of the pigs that have been brought to him in desperation when the owners couldn't cope any longer. He talks a lot of sense, providing information to would-be owners before they get their pigs and provides support and guidance to owners with regard to feeding, training, housing, behaviour and veterinary contacts.

If you want a pig that needs a good home and lots of love, contact him at www.potbelliedpigs.co.uk.

TIME TO SAY GOODBYE

If you are raising your pig as a pet, you will be happy to feed and nurture it for its lifetime. If you are raising it for meat, you will have to decide when and how you can end its life humanely.

Traditionally reared pigs mature later than intensively reared ones and will go to slaughter later. Because you have cared for and fed them well, the meat these pigs produce is of the highest quality.

If you are only producing pork for your own consumption, it is possible to have a pig killed at your home, but finding someone to do this is becoming more and more difficult. Also, because of a quirk in the law, any animal slaughtered at home must only be eaten by the owner. This means that legally, the owner's partner and children cannot consume the pork, nor can it be either given away or sold.

Your best bet is to find a local abbatoir — a registered one with appropriate hygiene facilities, where the staff are knowledgeable and the animals are treated as kindly as possible. Defra should be able to help you locate one. Since pigs are very given to stress, you will want to find one that is not too far away from your home if you can and try to make the journey as comfortable as possible. The same issues that you took into account when you brought your piglet home should be addressed here, except that you will definitely need a trailer for transport.

WHEN YOUR PIG DIES . . .

If you have a pet pig and it dies of old age (or any other reason), you can't just bury it in the garden as you would a hamster — it's against the law. Most pet crematoriums will cremate pigs. Providing you don't want 'pure ashes' (those that contain only your animal), the cost is not great — about £60. If you want to have a sole cremation, the cost is much higher; somewhere in the area of £130. Your vet should be able to give you advice about who to call and what you should do.

If you have a very sick pig and it needs to be put down, the usual method is to shoot it humanely. But since pigs are so intelligent, they are bound to know what is going to happen, so you might ask your vet if he could give it an injection and put it to sleep, which would be a much nicer way for your pig to depart the world.

BRITISH CUTS OF PORK

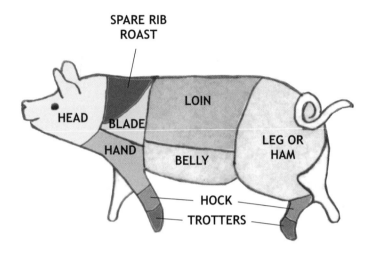

SPARE RIB ROAST

HEAD

BLADE

LOIN

HAND

BELLY

LEG OR HAM

HOCK

TROTTERS

In many parts of the world, the entire carcass (everything but the 'oink') is used, including the knuckle and cheek. In America, Scrapple is a savoury speciality of Pennsylvania, and its surrounding states, consisting of pork scraps and trimmings combined with maize meal and buckwheat flour, which are then formed into a loaf, sliced and fried. The Brazilian national dish, Feijoada, is prepared with pork trimmings: ears, tail and feet added to black beans, a variety of pork and beef products and at least two types of smoked sausage and jerked beef. British cooks are also now rediscovering some of the less prime cuts of the pig (such as pork belly, cheek and trotters), which, if properly cooked, are succulent and a great treat.

TROTTERS

Front and hind trotters or hocks can be cooked and eaten in soups or various other ways including pickled, in which the pig's feet are salted and smoked in the same manner as other pork cuts, such as ham. Pickled pigs' feet or trotters are then placed in large jars and covered with a hot brine solution. This preserving method allows the trotters to be stored without refrigeration until they are ready to be consumed.

EARS

Ears can be used in a number of ways, including salads, pickled and stewed. They are usually boiled first and then either baked or fried. Barbecued pigs' ears are also very tasty. Be sure to wash the ears well in lemon juice first. When they are cooked, the texture of the outside of the ear is gelatinous, like tofu, and the inside is quite crunchy. Pigs' ears feature in Japanese cuisine, where they are prepared by boiling or pickling and then served with vinegar. The ears can be eaten either hot or cold.

HOCKS

This is the part of the leg above the trotter below the 'hand' in the front and the leg or ham in the rear. Hocks are often used to flavour soups, such as pea soup, or braised or roasted and eaten at New Year's as 'soul food' with black beans and rice.

SLAB BACON

Unsliced bacon from the belly of the pig is called a slab. It usually comes with the rind on. If you like your bacon nice and thick, you can purchase a slab and cut it yourself. 450 g (1 lb) of slab bacon will yield about 6 thick rashers.

HEAD
Pigs' heads can be roasted and served with vegetables and some sort of barbecue sauce. This provides a lot of nice, crunchy skin and several different kinds of meat. Alternatively, to make brawn — a moulded, jellied cold meat that Americans call 'head cheese' — the head is simmered in a large stockpot until the meat is tender enough to fall off the bone. Then the meat is picked off and chopped. Seasonings such as sage or other herbs and a bit of lemon juice are added. The liquid used to boil the head is reduced to make the jelly in which the chopped meat is set. The mixture is then poured into moulds and refrigerated until it solidifies.

HAND /SHOULDER
Pork shoulder is above the front legs. Uses of this cut include braising, barbecuing, roasting and stewing. It can also be cured on the bone and used to make ham or sausages. Boned and cooked slowly, and sometimes stuffed, it also makes a very good roast.

LOIN
The loin is one of the prime cuts, from which tenderloin, loin chops, griskin (boned pork loin) and chump end of loin are cut as well as pork crown roasts, back ribs and pork steaks.

SPARE RIB ROAST/BLADE SHOULDER
This cut can be made into a rolled roast or cured and made into collar bacon.

LEGS/HAMS
From the leg there are chump chops, pork escalope and leg steaks. Common cuts of the leg include the rump (upper portion), centre and shank (lower portion). A whole pork leg is usually covered with skin and fat, and is typically prepared by roasting. Ham is cured and sometimes smoked and can be found either on or off the bone.

BELLY
The belly is the underside of the pig. It is often diced and used in stir-fries and is very popular in Chinese and Korean cuisine where it is marinated and cooked as a whole. It is also used in Sweet and Sour Pork, and can be rolled for roasting or used to make streaky bacon.

CHOPS
Pork chops are often cut perpendicular to the spine of the pig and usually contain a rib. The centre cut or pork loin chop includes a large T-shaped bone, similar to T-bone steak. Rib chops come from the rib portion of the loin and are similar to rib-eye steaks. Blade or shoulder chops come from the shoulder end of the loin.

SKIN
Pork Crackling is the British name for the salted crunchy pork rind produced when roasting a joint of pork. The heat of the oven causes the fatty pork

skin to dry, bubble up and become crunchy. The layer of fat underneath is retained, and can be eaten with the skin or removed. Some supermarkets sell just the layer of skin and fat (no meat), in a raw form for home grilling or roasting, or cooked and ready to eat from hot food counters.

Pork Scratchings is the British name for deep-fried salted crunchy pork rind with fat produced separately from the meat. This is then eaten cold. Pork scratchings are typically heavy, hard and have a crispy layer of fat under the skin; some still retain the hair of the pig and are flavoured only with salt. The pig hair is usually removed by quickly burning the skin of the pig before it is cut into pieces and cooked in hot fat. Hair removal is not totally effective, which is why some retain a few hairs. The hairs are what usually make people question the desirability of these pub snacks, but to some, these can also be highly desirable. Traditionally they were eaten as an accompaniment to a pint of beer in a pub, just like crisps and peanuts and were a sign of a genuine traditional British pub. Fewer and fewer pubs are offering them these days, however, some pubs that offer Sunday roast dinners are again producing homemade scratchings because their customers have demanded them.

RECIPES

INTRODUCTION

Charles Lamb (1775–1834) in *A Dissertation upon Roast Pig*, notes that according to a Chinese manuscript which his friend Thomas Manning, who not only travelled in China, but read and spoke the language, explained to him, 'Mankind for the first 70,000 years ate their meat raw, clawing or biting it from the living animal, just as they do in Abyssinia to this day'. The art of roasting, or rather grilling, was accidentally discovered in the following manner.

The swineherd Ho-ti, having gone out into the woods one morning to collect mast (food from forest trees) for his hogs, left his cottage in the care of his eldest son, Bo-bo, who, being fond of playing with fire, let some sparks escape into a bundle of straw, which kindling quickly, spread till the cottage was reduced to ashes. What was more important, a fine litter of newborn pigs perished. While the son was trying to figure out how to tell his father, he smelled something, but it wasn't the burnt cottage. He stooped down to feel a pig, testing to see if there was any life left in it and burnt his fingers. To cool them, he put them in his mouth. Some of the crumbs of scorched pig came away with his fingers and for the first time in his life (and the world's) he tasted crackling. When it dawned on him that this is what he had smelled and it tasted wonderful, he fell upon the pig, cramming crackling and flesh down his throat.

His father returned and started beating his son, but the blows weren't heeded; such was Bo-bo's delight at discovering burnt pig. He tried to get his father to taste it and after much pleading, thrust another piglet at him. After a while both father and son sat down to the mess and never left off until they had despatched all that remained of the litter.

Although Ho-ti swore Bo-bo to secrecy, the story got out (since Ho-ti's cottage now got burnt down more frequently than ever) and there was a trial. Evidence was given, the pig meat was produced in court and the foreman of the jury begged that some be handed over. He also burnt his fingers and tasted the pork. To the surprise of the whole court, they were pronounced not guilty.

Eventually it was discovered that pig might be cooked without burning down houses. Even if the above account is apocryphal, anyone who has eaten a beautifully roasted pig and its wonderful crackling would agree that it is almost worth burning your house down for!

Roast suckling pig is one of the most magnificent dishes in gastronomy; the closest that modern man can come to the ancient feasts of history when whole animals were brought in and laid on the festive table.

I have an old cookery book, *Feasts for All Seasons* written by the great gastronome and chef, Roy Andries de Groot, which includes a recipe for Suckling Pig that I made one New Year's Eve.

I won't include the recipe because not only does it

take two days to prepare, but my local butcher tells me it now costs as much to buy a suckling pig as it does a fully-grown one. I will, however, tell you the story.

THE NEW YEAR'S EVE FEAST

It was New Year's Eve and I had invited 12 friends to dinner. My main course was to be Suckling Pig. Never have so many disasters made such a wonderful dinner.

First hurdle: the pig was too big for my roasting tin. No problem. I bought a larger tin. Problem: it wouldn't quite fit in my oven. I decided to think about that later.

Second hurdle: while I was rinsing the pig in my kitchen sink, my two-year-old daughter toddled into the kitchen and demanded to 'pet the doggy'. I told her it wasn't a dog, it was a pig, but she wasn't having any of it. Through clenched teeth now, I kept repeating 'pig. It's a pig'. And she kept saying 'doggy. Want to pet the doggy'. So of course I lifted her up and let her pet it, silently wishing I was going to be cooking anything else.

Third hurdle: after preparing the pig for the oven and somehow managing to manhandle it into the roasting tin, I realised it was too heavy to lift. No problem. I called my husband. Both of us managed to get the tin in the oven, but of course the oven wouldn't quite close. So my husband's brilliant idea was to tie the oven closed with kitchen twine.

Every time I had to baste the darned pig (which had to be done religiously every 20 minutes), I had to untie the string. Since my pig weighed 9 kg (20 lb), this involved undoing and retying the string 15 times.

Fourth hurdle: do you have a serving dish large enough to put a whole (albeit baby) pig on? I didn't. So I covered my chopping board with aluminium foil, giving it a decorative raised edge. Clever!

My beautiful piglet was then garlanded with a cranberry necklace and presented with a polished red apple in her mouth. It was absolutely gorgeous and delicious. My friends thought so also. I took a photo of the finished dish . . . and never prepared suckling pig ever again.

SOUPS, STARTERS AND SNACKS

PANCETTA, FONTINA AND SAGE SCONES

You will need   **Makes 12—15**

75 g (3 oz) thinly sliced pancetta, chopped

225 g (8 oz) plain flour

15 ml (1 tbsp) baking powder

2.5 ml ($\frac{1}{2}$ tsp) salt

75 g (3 oz) unsalted butter, chilled and cut into
small cubes

115 g (4 oz) Fontina cheese, coarsely grated

15 ml (1 tbsp) chopped fresh sage leaves

200 ml (7 fl oz) buttermilk or 200 g (7 oz) plain
yoghurt, divided

Method

1. Preheat the oven to 230°C (450°F/Gas Mark 8).

2. Sauté the pancetta in a medium non-stick frying pan over a medium heat for about 7 minutes, until crisp. Remove from the heat and allow to cool.

3. Whisk the flour, baking powder and salt in a large bowl to blend. Rub in the butter with your fingertips until you have the consistency of breadcrumbs. Stir in the cheese and sage. Add all but 30 ml (2 tbsp) of the buttermilk or yogurt and the pancetta with any pan drippings and stir until moist clumps form.

4. Turn out onto a floured work surface and knead just until the dough holds together — about 5 or 6 turns. Flatten the dough to 2 cm ($\frac{3}{4}$ inch) and cut out rounds with a 5-cm (2-inch) biscuit cutter. Re-roll the dough and continue cutting out scones until all of the dough is used, trying not to overwork the dough. Transfer the scones to a large baking sheet, spacing them apart as they will spread. Brush the

tops of the scones with the remaining buttermilk or yoghurt.

5. Bake the scones until they are puffed and golden, 12–14 minutes. Serve warm with a cooked breakfast or with salad for a light lunch.

CHINESE LION'S HEAD SOUP

This is an easy version of a popular Chinese soup in which pak choi is simmered with homemade pork meatballs in a light chicken stock.

You will need   **Serves 4**

  450 g (1 lb) minced pork

  1 egg

  7.5 ml (1½ tsp) cornflour

  10 ml (2 tsp) sesame oil

  5 ml (1 tsp) finely chopped fresh ginger root

  5 ml (1 tsp) salt

  2 spring onions, chopped and divided

  15 ml (1 tbsp) vegetable oil

  1 head pak choi, chopped

  450 ml (¾ pint) chicken stock

  450 ml (¾ pint) water, or as needed

  15 ml (1 tbsp) soy sauce

  10 ml (2 tsp) sesame oil to drizzle

Method

1. Mix the pork, egg, cornflour, 10 ml (2 tsp) sesame oil, ginger, salt, and half of the chopped spring onions together in a bowl. Use your hands to mix until the ingredients are evenly distributed. Set aside.

2. Heat the vegetable oil in a wok or large frying pan over a high heat. When the oil is hot, sauté the

pak choi, stirring constantly, until it begins to wilt, 2—3 minutes. Pour in the chicken stock, water and soy sauce. Bring to the boil, then reduce the heat to medium.

3. Use a spoon to form the meat mixture into 2.5 cm (1 inch) balls. Drop them into the boiling soup. When the last ball has been added, cover with a lid and simmer for 10 minutes. Taste and adjust the seasoning. Serve garnished with the remaining spring onions and a drizzle of sesame oil.

PORK AND GINGER SOUP

You will need   Serves 4

25 ml (1$\frac{1}{2}$ tbsp) vegetable oil

$\frac{1}{4}$ small head of cabbage, shredded

115 g (4 oz) pork fillet, cut into thin strips

2 litres (3 pints) chicken stock

30 ml (2 tbsp) soy sauce

2.5 ml ($\frac{1}{2}$ tsp) finely chopped fresh ginger root

8 spring onions, chopped

160 g (5$\frac{3}{4}$ oz) instant Chinese noodles (2 packets)

Method

1. In a large frying pan or wok, heat the oil over a medium heat. Add the cabbage and pork; fry, stirring all the time until the pork is cooked, for approximately 5 minutes.

2. Add the chicken stock, soy sauce and ginger root. Bring to the boil. Reduce the heat to low and simmer for 10 minutes, stirring occasionally.

3. Stir in the spring onions and noodles and cook until the noodles are tender, 2—4 minutes. Serve immediately.

ENGLISH BREAKFAST FRITTATA

This is also ideal for a light lunch or supper.

You will need   Serves 4

  4 good quality pork chipolatas or 2 large pork sausages,
     cut into chunks
  4 rashers unsmoked back bacon
  150 g (5 oz) chestnut mushrooms, sliced
  6 large eggs, beaten
  Freshly ground black pepper
  8 cherry tomatoes, cut in half
  Grated Cheddar cheese
  Chopped parsley

Method
1. Preheat the oven to 200°C (400°F/Gas Mark 6).
2. Heat a non-stick ovenproof frying pan, add the
sausages and cook for 3 minutes. Add the bacon,
stirring for about 5 minutes, until it begins to crisp.
Add the mushrooms and continue to cook for
another 5 minutes or so. Drain the excess fat and
distribute the ingredients in the pan evenly.
3. Tip the eggs into the pan and season with
pepper. Lift the edges as you would an omelette,
so that the uncooked egg runs underneath. Cook
for a couple of minutes until the frittata sets. Add
the tomatoes and sprinkle with cheese.
4. Put the frying pan in the centre of the oven and
cook until the top of the frittata is just set.
Remove from the oven, sprinkle with parsley, cut
into 4 wedges and serve immediately.

JIAN JIA (CHINESE DUMPLINGS)

This is a traditional dish for Chinese New Year. You can make the filling the day before. You can also freeze the dumplings for three months prior to cooking. Just cook for a few minutes longer.

You will need   **Makes about 40**
For the Dumplings:
    350 g (12 oz) plain flour
    120 ml (4 fl oz) tepid water
    120 ml (4 fl oz) cold water

For the Filling:
    675 g (1½ lb) minced pork (not too lean)
    1 egg
    37.5 ml (2½ tbsp) cornflour
    5 ml (1 tsp) white wine or dry sherry
    450 g (1 lb) white cabbage, diced
    22.5 ml (1½ tbsp) thinly sliced spring onion
    5 ml (1 tsp) chopped fresh ginger root
    60 ml (4 tbsp) soy sauce
    5 ml (1 tsp) salt (or to taste)
    45 ml (3 tbsp) sesame oil
    45 ml (3 tbsp) peanut or vegetable oil

Method
1. Add the tepid water to the flour and stir well, then add the cold water. Knead the dough, cover it with a towel, and let it sit for at least 20 minutes.
2. Make the filling. In a bowl, mix together thoroughly the pork, egg, cornflour, wine or sherry, cabbage, spring onion, ginger root, soy sauce, salt and sesame oil.

3. Turn the dough onto a lightly floured cutting board and knead until it is smooth. Cut the dough into 40 equal pieces. Use your hand to flatten each piece of dough, and roll it into a thin pancake approximately 7.5 cm (3 inches) in diameter.

4. Put 15 ml (1 tbsp) of the filling in the centre of each dumpling and fold in half, to form a crescent shape. Press the edges with the tines of a fork to seal.

5. Heat a frying pan and add 45 ml (3 tbsp) peanut or vegetable oil. When the oil is hot, add the dumplings, cooking a few at a time (they should not touch). Cover the pan and cook the dumplings on a high heat for 5 minutes. Sprinkle with cold water, cover quickly and cook for another five minutes. (Adding cold water will steam the top of the dumplings). Turn the dumplings and repeat until they are golden brown, about three turns. Serve hot with soy sauce or chilli dipping sauce or make this ginger soy sauce, a traditional dumpling dip.

GINGER SOY SAUCE

You will need

    60 ml (4 tbsp) soy sauce
    60 ml (4 tbsp) rice or balsamic vinegar
    30 ml (2 tbsp) water
    15 ml (1 tbsp) peeled, julienne ginger root, soaked in
        ice water.
    1.5 ml ($1/4$ tsp) hot pepper flakes (optional)

Combine all the ingredients in a small bowl. Mix thoroughly and serve. This sauce will keep for up to 1 week in the refrigerator, without the ginger root. Add the ginger root when ready to serve.

MARINATED PORK BITES

You will need   **Serves 8—12**

900 g (2 lb) boneless pork cut into 2 cm ($^3/_4$-inch) cubes

30 ml (2 tbsp) brown sugar

30 ml (2 tbsp) hoisin sauce

30 ml (2 tbsp) soy sauce

15 ml (1 tbsp) Worcestershire sauce

15 ml (1 tbsp) toasted sesame oil

1 shallot, chopped

10 ml (2 tsp) Chinese five spice powder

10 ml (2 tsp) grated fresh ginger root

2 cloves garlic, crushed

Method

1. In a large self-seal plastic bag, combine all ingredients and mix well. Close the bag and marinate in the refrigerator for 8—12 hours.

2. Preheat the oven to 180°C (350°F/Gas Mark 4). Remove the pork cubes from the marinade, discarding the marinade. Pat the pork dry with kitchen paper.

3. Place the pork cubes in a single layer in a shallow roasting tin and bake for 25—30 minutes, until the pork is tender and lightly browned. Remove to a serving dish, pierce each cube with a wooden toothpick and serve hot with drinks or as a starter.

BACON AND LEEK QUICHE

I have made this with bacon that was left over from Sunday breakfast, and it was just as good as when you cook the bacon to order.

You will need   **Serves 4—6**

500 g (1 lb 2 oz) shortcrust pastry, home-made
   or purchased

225 g (8 oz) dry cure bacon (streaky or back, cut
   into pieces)

175 g (6 oz) young leeks, trimmed, washed and
   thinly sliced

150 ml (5 fl oz) double cream

300 ml (10 fl oz) milk

3 large eggs

150 g (5 oz) mature Cheddar cheese or Gruyère
   cheese, grated

Paprika, to sprinkle

Rocket salad, to serve

Method

1. Preheat the oven to 200°C (400°F/Gas Mark 6)

2. Roll out the pastry on a floured board and use to line a 23 cm (9 inch) flan tin. Prick the base, line with parchment paper, fill with baking beans and bake for 10 minutes. Remove the baking beans and parchment and bake for a further 5—10 minutes, until light golden in colour. Remove from the oven to cool.

3. Reduce the oven temperature to 180°C (350°F/ Gas Mark 4).

4. Cook the bacon in a non-stick frying pan for 5 minutes until golden. Drain on kitchen paper.

Add the leeks to the pan and cook for a further
5 minutes.

5. In a bowl, beat together the cream, milk, eggs
and most of the cheese. Scatter the leeks and
bacon on the base of the partially baked pastry
case and pour over the cream mixture. Sprinkle
with the rest of the cheese and dust with paprika.

6. Bake for 30—35 minutes until the filling is just
set. Remove from the oven and let cool for 15
minutes before cutting into wedges. This is very
nice served with a rocket salad.

BACON AND ONION TART

You will need   **Serves 6**

   8 bacon rashers, chopped

   3 large onions, sliced

   1 large egg

   115 g (4 oz) soured cream or crème fraîche

   5 ml (1 tsp) salt

   2.5 ml (½ tsp) freshly-ground black pepper

   Pinch of ground nutmeg

   400—450 g (14—16 oz) pizza dough, homemade or bought

   1.25 ml (¼ tsp) caraway seeds

Method

1. Preheat the oven to 190°C (375°F/Gas Mark 5).
Sauté the bacon in a large frying pan over a
medium-high heat until slightly crisp. Drain all
but 15 ml (1 tbsp) bacon drippings from the pan.
Add onions to the bacon and sauté over a medium
heat until the onions are very soft, but not brown,
for about 10 minutes. Cool.

2. Whisk the egg, soured cream or crème fraîche,

salt, pepper and nutmeg in a large bowl to blend.
Stir in the cooled onion mixture.

3. Roll the pizza dough out on lightly floured surface
to a 32.5 x 25 cm (13 x 10 inch) rectangle. Turn the
edges up to make a 1 cm (½ inch) rim. Transfer to a
baking sheet. Spread the onion mixture over the
dough and sprinkle with caraway seeds.

4. Bake the tart until the onion custard is set and
the crust is golden brown around the edges and
brown on the bottom, about 25 minutes.

TARTIFLETTE WITH BRIE AND BACON

*This dish is usually made with reblochon cheese,
but it is just as tasty made with creamy Brie,
combined with smoked bacon and potatoes.*

You will need   Serves 6—8

   10 ml (2 tsp) vegetable oil

   300 g (11 oz) smoked rindless back bacon, chopped

   1 large onion, thinly sliced

   Fresh thyme sprigs

   300 ml (10 fl oz) double cream

   300 ml (10 fl oz) milk

   1 clove garlic, crushed

   1 kg (2.2 lb) waxy potatoes, peeled and thinly sliced

   Freshly ground black pepper

   250 g (9 oz) ripe Brie cheese, cut into thin slices

Method

1. Heat the oven to 180°C (350°F/Gas Mark 4) and
lightly grease a 1.5 litre (2½ pint) ovenproof dish.

2. Heat the oil in a frying pan and fry the bacon
and onion over a medium heat for 4—5 minutes
until beginning to brown.

3. Chop the thyme leaves, reserving a few for garnish. Place the thyme, cream, milk and garlic in a large pan. Bring to the simmer, add the potatoes, then cover and cook for 5 minutes. Stir in the bacon and onions and season with freshly ground black pepper. Place half the potato mixture in the base of the prepared dish, then top with half the sliced cheese. Repeat, finishing with a layer of cheese.

4. Bake in the oven for 40–45 minutes, until the potatoes are tender when pierced with a knife, and the top is golden. Garnish with the remaining thyme and serve with a green salad and crusty bread.

MAIN COURSES

CROWN ROAST OF PORK WITH AWESOME SAUSAGE, APPLE AND CRANBERRY STUFFING

One Christmas, tired of turkey, I made this for our festive dinner. I adapted my eldest daughter's favourite turkey stuffing and the result was just fantastic!

You will need   Serves 8

16 rib crown roast of pork (about 3.5 kg/8 lb)

30 ml (2 tbsp) butter

30 ml (2 tbsp) flour

450 ml ($^3/_4$) pint dry white wine or French vermouth

1 pork or chicken stock cube

5 ml (1 tsp) dried thyme (optional)

For the stuffing:

225 g (8 oz) wholemeal bread cubes

450 g (1 lb) sausage meat

1 large onion, chopped

3 French shallots, chopped

10 ml (2 tsp) dried sage

7.5 ml (1$^1/_2$ tsp) dried rosemary

2.5 ml ($^1/_2$ tsp) dried thyme

1 crisp apple, peeled, cored and chopped

75 g (3 oz) dried cranberries

Handful of fresh parsley, chopped

1 chicken liver, cooked and chopped

175 ml (6 fl oz) chicken or pork stock

50 g (2 oz) butter, melted

Method

1. First make the stuffing. Preheat the oven to 180°C (350°F/Gas Mark 4). Spread the bread cubes

in a single layer on a large baking sheet and bake for 5—7 minutes, until evenly toasted. Tip the bread cubes into a large bowl. Leave the oven on if you will be cooking the pork now.

2. In a large frying pan, cook the sausage meat and onions over a medium heat, stirring and breaking up the lumps until evenly browned. Add the shallots, sage, rosemary and thyme. Cook, stirring, for 2 minutes to blend flavours.

3. Pour the sausage mixture over the bread cubes in the bowl. Mix in the chopped apple, dried cranberries, parsley and liver. Drizzle with stock and melted butter and mix lightly.

4. If not using immediately, cover the mixture and refrigerate until ready to use. Otherwise, prepare the pork for roasting.

5. Cover a roasting rack with aluminium foil and place in a roasting tin. Place the roast, bone ends up, on the rack. Roast the pork for 1 hour. Remove from the oven.

6. Spoon as much of the stuffing that will fit into the centre of the pork and cover loosely with aluminium foil. Put the rest of the stuffing into a suitable buttered baking dish.

7. Roast the pork until a thermometer inserted into the centre of the pork registers 65°C (150°F), about 1 hour, basting with the pan juices every so often to moisten. The extra stuffing will only need about 30 minutes cooking time, so don't forget to remove it when it is thoroughly heated.

8. While the pork is roasting, make the sauce. Melt the butter in a saucepan and add the flour. Stir and cook for 1 minute. Crumble the stock cube into the wine or vermouth and add to the roux. Add the

thyme, if using. Cook the sauce, stirring constantly until it is thickened. Keep warm and serve with the pork and stuffing.

N.B. I don't like very thick sauces, so I tend not to add as much flour to the roux as some people, but you should adjust the amount to your taste.

BACON-WRAPPED MAPLE PORK LOIN

You will need   **Serves 8**
For brining pork:

   2 litres (3$^{1}/_{2}$ pints) water

   65 g (2$^{1}/_{2}$ oz) coarse sea salt

   30 ml (2 tbsp) pure maple syrup

   2.5 ml ($^{1}/_{2}$ tsp) crushed black peppercorns

   2 sprigs fresh sage

   1 large garlic clove, smashed

   1 fresh bay leaf

   1.8–2 kg (4–4$^{1}/_{2}$ lb) boneless pork loin roast, trimmed

For roasting pork:

   3 garlic cloves, finely chopped

   30 ml (2 tbsp) finely chopped fresh sage

   45 ml (3 tbsp) pure maple syrup, divided

   16 streaky bacon rashers (about 450 g/1 lb)

   15 ml (1 tbsp) cider vinegar

   2.5 ml ($^{1}/_{2}$ tsp) cornflour

   5 ml (1 tsp) water

Method

1. Brine the pork: combine all brining ingredients except the pork loin in a 3- to 4-litre (5–7 pint) saucepan and heat over a high heat, stirring, until

the salt is dissolved. Pour the brine into a deep 4-litre (7-pint) pot; cool to room temperature, uncovered, for about 2 hours.

2. Add the pork to the brine, ensuring it is completely covered by brine, and marinate, covered, in the refrigerator for 8—24 hours.

3. To roast the pork. Preheat the oven to 180°C (350°F/Gas Mark 4). Pat the pork dry (discard brine) and remove any strings, then transfer to a roasting tin. Stir together the garlic, sage, and 15 ml (1 tbsp) maple syrup in a small bowl and rub all over the pork. Lay bacon slices crossways over the pork, overlapping slightly, and tuck the ends of the bacon underneath the pork.

4. Roast the pork until an oven thermometer registers 60°C (140°F), about 1¼ hours. Stir together 15 ml (1 tbsp) maple syrup and the vinegar until combined. Brush the maple mixture over the bacon and continue to roast the pork until the thermometer registers 70°C (150°F), for about 10 minutes more. Remove from the oven and let stand in the tin for 15 minutes. Transfer the roast to a cutting board, reserving juices in the tin, and let it stand, uncovered, while making the sauce.

5. Skim fat from the pan juices and discard, then transfer juices to a small saucepan and bring to the simmer. Stir together the cornflour and water and whisk into the juices. Simmer, stirring, until slightly thickened, for about 1 minute. Remove from the heat and stir in the remaining maple syrup. Serve the pork with the sauce.

INDONESIAN SPICED PORK

You will need   **Serves 4**

450 g (1 lb) boneless pork loin, cut into strips

15 ml (1 tbsp) sunflower oil

15 ml (1 tbsp) fresh lemon juice

5–10 ml (1–2 tsp) Shoarma spice mix (*see below*)

Salt, to taste

Pitta bread to serve

SHOARMA SPICE MIX

You will need   **Makes 1 small jarful**

15 ml (1 tbsp) cumin seeds

15 ml (1 tbsp) coriander seeds

15 ml (1 tbsp) garlic powder

7.5 ml (1½ tsp) paprika

5 ml (1 tsp) ground turmeric

2.5 ml (½ tsp) ground cloves

2.5 ml (½ tsp) cayenne pepper

5 ml (1 tsp) ground ginger

5 ml (1 tsp) ground black pepper

2.5 ml (½ tsp) ground cinnamon

Method

1. Fry the cumin and coriander seeds in a frying pan, stirring for a few minutes, until they are fragrant, but do not allow them to burn. Remove from the heat and let cool, then grind as finely as possible.

2. When cool, mix the ground cumin and coriander with the rest of the ingredients and store in a small airtight jar.

For the pork:
1. Marinate the pork in the oil, lemon juice and spice mix, adding salt to taste, for several hours or overnight in the refrigerator.
2. Grill or stir-fry, adding onions or peppers if you like to the stir-fry mixture.
3. Spread the pitta bread with tzatziki (cucumber salad) or mayonnaise and stuff with the pork mixture.

N.B. Shoarma spice mix is very versatile. It can be used in marinades, or as a dry rub for beef, lamb or chicken as well as pork.

ITALIAN PORK LOIN WITH POTATO GRATIN

You will need   **Serves 4—6**

For *the pork*:
  1.8 kg (4 lb) boned pork loin, skin scored
  75 ml (6 tbsp) chopped sage
  75 ml (6 tbsp) chopped fresh rosemary leaves,
      plus 6 sprigs of rosemary
  5 garlic cloves, chopped
  120 ml (4 fl oz) olive oil
  Salt and freshly-ground black pepper
  Kitchen string to tie up the roast
  3 onions, quartered
  3 fennel bulbs, quartered
  30 ml (2 tbsp) olive oil
  200ml (7 fl oz) dry Italian white wine

For the potato gratin:
  500g (1 lb 2 oz) potatoes, peeled and very thinly sliced

2 onions, sliced

1 garlic clove, chopped

15 ml (1 tbsp) chopped fresh rosemary leaves

Salt and freshly-ground black pepper

300 ml (10 fl oz) hot chicken stock

Method

1. Preheat the oven to 180°C (350°F/Gas Mark 5).

2. Lay the pork out, skin side down. Mix together the sage, rosemary, garlic, 90 ml (3 fl oz) of the olive oil, salt and pepper in a small bowl. Rub this thoroughly over the pork flesh. Roll up the meat and tie with kitchen string. Rub salt into the scored skin. (This will make the crackling really crisp).

3. Spread the onions and fennel in the bottom of a roasting tin. Drizzle over 30 ml (2 tbsp) olive oil. Place the pork on top and add the rosemary sprigs.

4. Roast the pork in the oven for 1½ hours in total. After 1 hour pour 100ml (3½ fl oz) wine into the roasting tin around the pork. If the crackling is starting to burn, cover loosely with aluminium foil.

5. Meanwhile, layer the sliced potatoes in a shallow ovenproof dish with the sliced onions, garlic, rosemary and salt and pepper. Pour over the hot stock. Bake for 1 hour until the potatoes are tender. Remove from the oven and keep warm.

6. When the pork is done, remove it from the oven and place on a serving dish, surrounded by the fennel and onion. Keep warm. Pour the juices from the tin into a saucepan and reduce to half. Add the remaining wine, season with salt and pepper and reduce further until you like the taste and consistency.

7. Serve the pork with some of the reduced sauce, accompanied by the potato gratin.

STIR-FRIED THAI PORK WITH PEANUT SAUCE AND VEGETABLES

This is a great Oriental pork dish. It doesn't take long, it's very good, and it's a healthy choice. You will need Thai peanut sauce, which you can buy at the supermarket or source a recipe from the internet.

You will need   **Serves 4**

   30 ml (2 tbsp) vegetable oil

   900 g (2 lb) boneless pork loin

   2 red peppers, diced

   280 g (10 oz) mushrooms, sliced

   1/2 head of pak choi, chopped

   2 yellow courgettes, thinly sliced

   2 cloves garlic, finely chopped

   3 spring onions, snipped into pieces

   Thai peanut sauce

   55 g (2 oz) dry roasted peanuts

Method

1. Add 15 ml (1 tbsp) oil to a large frying pan or wok. Sauté the pork until it is just done. Remove from the pan and set aside.

2. Add the remaining oil to the pan. Sauté the peppers, mushrooms, pak choi, courgettes, garlic and spring onions until just tender.

3. Add the pork back to the pan. Add peanut sauce to taste — at least enough to coat the ingredients. Cook and stir for another 2—3 minutes adding more sauce if necessary. Add the roasted peanuts.

4. Serve with rice and an exotic fruit salad.

TINGA POBLANO
(Smoky Pork Stew)

You will need   **Serves 4**

5 ml (1 tsp) corn oil

250 g (9 oz) boneless pork loin, cut into cubes

50 g (2 oz) chorizo, sliced

115 g (4 oz) onions, chopped

1 large garlic clove

450 g (1 lb) red potatoes, cut into cubes

400 g (14 oz) tinned chopped tomatoes

250 ml (8 fl oz) chicken stock

2 bay leaves

5 ml (1 tsp) tinned chipotle peppers in adobo sauce

2.5 ml ($\frac{1}{2}$ tsp) granulated sugar

2.5 ml ($\frac{1}{2}$ tsp) salt

Pinch each of dried thyme, marjoram and oregano

5 ml (1 tsp) cornflour, dissolved in 15 ml (1 tbsp) cold
    water

1 medium red onion, thinly sliced

$\frac{1}{2}$ small avocado, peeled and thinly sliced

40 g (1$\frac{1}{2}$ oz) feta cheese, crumbled

Method

1. Heat the oil in a large non-stick frying pan and
add the pork, chorizo and chopped onions. Cook
over a medium-high heat, stirring occasionally, for
8–10 minutes, until lightly browned. Add the garlic
and cook for a further 2 minutes. Add the
potatoes, tomatoes, chicken stock, bay leaves,
chipotle peppers, sugar, salt, thyme, marjoram and
oregano. Bring to the boil, reduce the heat to low
and simmer, covered, for 15–20 minutes until the
potatoes are cooked.

2. Stir the cornflour mixture into the pork. Simmer, uncovered, stirring frequently, for 5 minutes, until the sauce is slightly thickened. Remove and discard the bay leaves.

3. Meanwhile, mix together the red onion, avocado and feta cheese in a small bowl.

4. Serve the stew with a portion of the onion-avocado-cheese mixture.

PORK TENDERLOIN WITH ORANGE, SHERRY AND SAGE SAUCE

Pork tenderloin is a versatile meat that lends itself well to a variety of seasoning and sauce variations. The pungent flavours of orange and sage complement the pork perfectly and make a wonderful main course for an autumn dinner party.

You will need

Cooking spray

2 pork tenderloins, about 350 g (12 oz) each

Salt and freshly-ground black pepper

15 ml (1 tbsp) olive oil, divided

2 medium shallots, finely chopped

75 ml (5 tbsp) dry sherry

250 ml (8 fl oz) freshly-squeezed orange juice

Grated rind of 1 orange

7.5 ml (1½ tsp) cornflour

1 orange, peeled, seeded and cut into chunks

6–8 fresh sage leaves, finely chopped

1. Preheat the oven to 220°C (425°F/Gas Mark 7). Line a shallow roasting tin with aluminium foil and spritz with cooking spray.

2. Remove any excess fat from the tenderloins. Place them in the foil-lined tin, drizzle with about 5 ml (1 tsp) of the olive oil and season with salt and pepper. Place in the oven and roast for 20 minutes.

3. While the pork roasts, heat the remaining olive oil in a frying pan over a medium heat. Add the chopped shallot and cook until softening, for about 1 minute. Add the sherry, orange juice and orange rind and bring to the simmer.

4. Mix the cornflour with a small quantity of water until it is dissolved. Add to the simmering orange-sherry sauce and stir until the sauce begins to thicken. Add the orange chunks and chopped sage leaves, reduce the heat to low and remove 30 ml (2 tbsp) of the sauce for glazing the pork.

5. Remove the pork from the oven and brush the reserved sauce over the top. Return to the oven for 3–5 minutes, or until an instant read thermometer registers 65°C (150°F). Transfer to a cutting board, cover loosely with foil and allow to rest for about 5 minutes.

6. Slice the pork and place on a serving dish with some sauce on top. Serve extra sauce on the side.

PARMESAN PORK TENDERLOIN

You will need   **Serves 4**

    2 x 400 g (2 x 14 oz) pork tenderloins

    Salt and freshly-ground pepper

    85 g (3 oz) freshly grated Parmesan cheese

    30 ml (2 tbsp) ground cumin

1. Preheat the oven to 190°C (375°F/Gas Mark 5).

2. Pat the pork tenderloins dry with kitchen paper and lightly season with salt and pepper.

3. In a small bowl, mix together the cheese and cumin. Press the mixture over the pork, coating it as thoroughly as possible.

4. Put the pork on a baking sheet or in a shallow roasting tin. Bake for 12 minutes. Turn over and bake for a further 10 minutes (the pork should be slightly pink in the centre). Remove from the oven, transfer to a cutting board and allow to rest for 15 minutes.

5. Cut the pork into thick slices and serve with mash and an appropriate vegetable.

PORK TENDERLOIN WITH RHUBARB CHUTNEY

You will need   **Serves 4**
For the chutney:

    150 g (5 oz) granulated sugar

    75 ml (5 tbsp) cider vinegar

    5 ml (1 tsp) grated fresh ginger root

    7.5 ml (1½ tsp) garlic powder

    2.5 ml (½ tsp) ground cumin

    1.25 ml (¼ tsp) ground cinnamon

    1.25 ml (¼ tsp) ground cloves

    1.25 ml (¼ tsp) chilli powder

    500 g (1 lb 2 oz) rhubarb, diced

    75 g (3 oz) red onion, chopped

    50 g (2 oz) sultanas

For the pork:

    675 g (1½ lb) pork tenderloin

    5 ml (1 tsp) ground cumin

    Salt and freshly-ground black pepper

    15 ml (1 tbsp) olive oil

    4 sprigs fresh coriander, to garnish

1. To make the chutney, combine the sugar, vinegar, ginger, garlic, cumin, cinnamon, cloves and chilli powder in a large saucepan. Bring to the simmer over a low heat, stirring occasionally, until the sugar dissolves. Add the rhubarb, onion and raisins. Increase heat to medium-high and cook until the rhubarb is tender and the mixture thickens slightly. Remove from heat and let cool completely.

2. Preheat the oven to 200°C (400°F/Gas Mark 6).

3. Sprinkle the pork with cumin, salt and pepper. Heat the oil in a large, heavy frying pan over a high heat. Add the pork and brown on all sides, for about 5 minutes.

4. Transfer the pork to a roasting tin. Brush with 90 ml (6 tbsp) of the chutney. Place in the preheated oven, brushing occasionally with more chutney. Cook until an instant read thermometer inserted into the centre registers 65°C (155°F), for about 25 minutes. Slice the pork into medallions. Garnish with coriander sprigs. Serve with remaining chutney.

PORK CHOPS SALMORIGLIO

'Salmoriglio' refers to a strong, fragrant sauce from Sicily, which is also great on chicken, lamb, beef and fish.

You will need   **Serves 4—6**

    120 ml (4 fl oz) extra virgin olive oil

    30 ml (2 tbsp) finely chopped fresh oregano

    30 ml (2 tbsp) finely chopped fresh thyme

    30 ml (2 tbsp) lemon juice

    15 ml (1 tbsp) grated lemon rind

    Salt and freshly-ground black pepper to taste

    4—6 pork chops, about 2 cm (3/4 inch) thick

1. Combine the oil, herbs, lemon juice and rind, salt and pepper in an electric blender or food processor and process until the sauce is emulsified.
2. Heat the grill to high. Season the pork chops with salt and pepper and grill until done — about 5—7 minutes per side. Spoon the sauce over the chops, or serve it on the side for diners to help themselves.

Recipe reproduced by permission of Worldwide Recipes www.worldwiderecipes.com

SPICED KUROBUTA PORK CHOPS

Three hundred years after Oliver Cromwell tasted some delicious pork in Berkshire, pork from the Berkshire breed has regained popularity with modern diners not only in the UK, but in Japan, where it is known as kurobuta. This is pork as it was meant to taste — juicy and flavourful. Don't worry if you can't source Aleppo pepper or Malabar peppercorns. It will still be delicious.

You will need   **Serves 4**

15 ml (1 tbsp) ground Aleppo pepper

15 ml (1 tbsp) Hungarian sweet paprika

10 ml (2 tsp) coarse sea salt

10 ml (2 tsp) whole Malabar peppercorns, freshly ground

5 ml (1 tsp) chopped fresh sage leaves

4 kurobuta/Berkshire bone-in rib chops, about 4 cm (1$\frac{1}{2}$ inches) thick, 275—350 g (10—12 oz) each

75 ml (5 tbsp) olive oil

Flour to dredge

Fruity sauce of your choice to serve, or see next page

Method

1. Preheat the oven to 350°C (180°F/Gas Mark 4).
2. Mix the pepper, paprika, salt, ground peppercorns and sage together in a small bowl.
3. Brush the pork chops on both sides with 30 ml (2 tbsp) of the oil. Sprinkle the pork generously with the spice mixture, pressing it down to adhere.
4. Spoon some flour into a plastic bag and dredge the pork chops in it, shaking off the excess flour.
5. Heat the remaining oil in a large ovenproof frying pan over a medium-high heat. Add the pork and brown on all sides, for about 5–6 minutes in all.
6. Transfer the frying pan to the oven and bake until an instant-read thermometer registers 63°C (145°F).
7. Serve with garlic mash and a simple fruity sauce. In a small saucepan put 5 ml (1 tsp) cornflour stirred into 15 ml (1 tbsp) water. Add 300 ml (10 fl oz) pomegranate juice, a spoonful or two of cider vinegar and a pinch of ground cardamom. Heat gently until thickened and season with salt and pepper to taste.

OVEN-BARBECUED SPARE RIBS

You will need   **Serves 4**

900 g (2lb) pork spareribs

90ml (6 tbsp) molasses or black treacle

1 garlic clove, crushed

15 ml (1 tbsp) tomato purée

5 ml (1 tsp) French or English mustard

15 ml (1 tbsp) cider vinegar

2.5 ml ($\frac{1}{2}$ tsp) dried thyme

Cayenne pepper

Salt and freshly-ground black pepper

Method

1. Preheat the oven to 190°C (375°F/Gas Mark 5). Separate the spare ribs into single ribs.

2. In a small mixing bowl, combine the molasses, garlic, tomato purée, mustard, vinegar, thyme, salt, pepper and cayenne pepper. Mix thoroughly.

3. Arrange the spareribs in a single layer in a large roasting tin. Brush them lightly with a little of the barbecue sauce, then roast for 30 minutes, turning occasionally.

4. Remove the spareribs from the tin and pour off all the fat. Return the spareribs to the tin and spoon over the remaining sauce. Roast for a further hour, basting frequently, until the ribs are glazed and golden brown.

BRAISED PORK WITH BLACK GRAPES AND BALSAMIC VINEGAR

You will need   Serves 4—6

800 g (1¾ lb) boneless pork shoulder trimmed,
   cut into 3 equal pieces

Salt and freshly-ground black pepper

60 ml (4 tbsp) olive oil, divided

8 large shallots, halved, cut into thin slices

450 g (1 lb) seedless black grapes

30 ml (2 tbsp) granulated sugar

120 ml (4 fl oz) balsamic vinegar

450 ml (¾ pint) chicken stock

2 fresh sage sprigs

4 fresh thyme sprigs

2 fresh rosemary sprigs

Method

1. Preheat the oven to 160°C (325°F/Gas Mark 3).
Sprinkle the pork with salt and pepper.

2. Heat 30 ml (2 tbsp) of the oil in a large
ovenproof pot over a medium-high heat. Add the
pork to the pot and brown on all sides, for about
10 minutes. Transfer the pork to a plate and drain
fat from the pot.

3. Heat the remaining oil in the same pot over a
medium heat. Add the shallots and grapes; sauté
until the shallots are golden, stirring occasionally
for about 3 minutes. Add the sugar; sauté for
30 seconds. Add the vinegar, bring the mixture to
the boil and cook until slightly reduced, for about
3 minutes. Add the stock, herb sprigs and pork with
its juices from the plate. Bring to the boil.

4. Cover the pot and transfer to the oven. Braise the

pork for 1 hour. Using tongs, turn the pork over and continue braising until the meat is very tender — about 45 minutes longer. With a slotted spoon, transfer the pork to a serving dish and cover loosely with aluminium foil.

5. Remove the herb sprigs from the pot and skim fat from the cooking liquid. Boil over a high heat until thickened for about 7 minutes. Season the sauce with salt and pepper. Pour over the pork, portion and serve.

SRI LANKAN PORK CURRY

The original recipe uses a pandanus leaf, but since it is not obtainable in the UK my Sri Lankan neighbour, who is a very good cook, suggested that I substitute lemongrass. She also said that a little sugar stirred in at the end is a good touch.

You will need   **Serves 4—6**
For the roasted curry powder:
   15 ml (1 tbsp) coriander seeds
   7.5 ml (1$^1/_2$ tsp) cumin seeds
   1.25 ml ($^1/_4$ tsp) fenugreek seeds
   2.5 ml ($^1/_2$ tsp) fennel seeds
   2.5 cm (1-inch) cinnamon stick
   3 whole cloves
   5 cardamom seeds
   20 curry leaves
   5 cm (2-inch) lemongrass
   2 hot dried chillies

For the curry:
   2 medium onions, chopped

2.5 cm (1-inch) fresh ginger root, chopped

4 cloves garlic, chopped

30 ml (2 tbsp) vegetable oil

12 curry leaves

7.5 cm (3-inch) cinnamon stick

4 cardamom pods

900g (2 lb) pork shoulder, cut into large cubes

15 ml (1 tbsp) red wine vinegar

45g (1^1/$_2$ oz) tamarind paste, mixed with 240 ml (8 fl oz) hot water then sieved (you will only use the liquid)

300ml (10 fl oz) thick coconut milk

2.5 ml (^{1}/$_2$ tsp) granulated sugar

Steamed jasmine rice, to serve

Method

1. Make the roasted curry powder: heat a heavy frying pan over a medium heat. Add all the ingredients except the curry leaves, lemongrass and chillies. Fry, stirring constantly, until all the spices are well browned.

2. Add the curry leaves, lemongrass and chillies and continue stirring until they have begun to brown and the rest of the spices are a dark brown, but don't allow them to burn.

3. Tip the contents of the pan into a bowl and allow to cool for a few minutes, then grind to a powder with a spice grinder or pestle and mortar. Leave to cool completely and store in an airtight jar.

4. Make the curry. Put the onions, ginger and garlic into a food processor and whiz together until finely chopped.

5. Heat the oil in a large saucepan or wok and add the curry leaves. Stir for a few seconds then add

the onion mixture. Fry until beginning to colour,
then add the cinnamon stick, cardamom pods and
45 ml (3 tbsp) of the roasted curry powder. Fry for
another minute.

6. Add the pork to the pan and stir until coated
with the spice mixture. Add the vinegar and
tamarind liquid and season with salt. Bring to a
slow simmer, then cover and leave to simmer for
about 1 hour until the pork is very tender.

7. Stir in the coconut milk and cook for a further
15 minutes. Add the sugar. Taste and adjust
seasoning and serve with steamed jasmine rice.

PORK CHILLI

This is a delicious new take on Chilli, using pork
instead of the usual beef.

You will need   Serves 4—6

15 ml (1 tbsp) olive oil

225 g (8 oz) lean minced pork

225 g (8 oz) onions, chopped

2 cloves garlic, finely chopped

115 g (4 oz) mushrooms, chopped

225 g (8 oz) green beans

225 g (8 oz) fresh or frozen peas

1/2 green pepper, chopped

1/2 red pepper, chopped

400 g (14 oz) passata

Chilli powder to taste

Ground nutmeg to taste

Dried marjoram to taste

Salt to taste

Crusty bread to serve

Method

1. Heat the olive oil in a large, deep frying pan over a medium heat and cook the pork until evenly browned. Reserving the juices in the pan, remove pork, and set aside.

2. Stir the onions and garlic into the pan and cook in the pork juices over a medium heat until tender. Mix in the mushrooms, green beans, peas and green and red peppers. Cook, stirring until tender and heated through.

3. Return the pork to the pan. Mix in the passata. Season with chilli powder, nutmeg, marjoram, and salt. Reduce heat and simmer about 45 minutes to allow the flavours to blend. Serve with crusty bread.

CANADIAN PORK TOURTIÈRE

The word 'tourtière' in French actually means a round dish for making 'tourtes', or pies. Somehow it came to represent the pies themselves in French-speaking Canada.

You will need   Serves 6—8

675 g (1½ lb) minced lean pork

120 ml (4 fl oz) white wine or water

1 medium onion, finely chopped

1-3 cloves garlic, finely chopped

5 ml (1 tsp) celery seeds

2.5 ml (½ tsp) dried sage

Pinch of ground cloves

Salt and freshly-ground black pepper to taste

3 medium potatoes, boiled and mashed

Pastry for a 2-crust 23-cm (9-inch) pie, bought or homemade

Method

1. Combine all ingredients except the potatoes and pastry in a large saucepan over a moderate heat, and cook until the meat is lightly browned. Cover and simmer for 45 minutes.

2. Stir in the mashed potatoes and let cool. Line a 23-cm (9-inch) pie dish with half the pastry and fill with the cooled pork mixture. Top with the remaining pastry and crimp the edges. Cut 2 or 3 vents in the top of the pie.

3. Preheat the oven to 230°C (450°F/Gas Mark 8) and bake for 10 minutes. Reduce the heat to 180°C (350°F/Gas Mark 4) and bake for an additional 30 minutes.

Recipe reproduced by permission of Worldwide Recipes www.worldwiderecipes.com

HOMEMADE SAUSAGES

This is a very basic recipe for sausages. My butcher won't be coaxed into giving out his secret recipe for Malmesbury Sausages, but you can add herbs and spices such as parsley, chervil, sage, chilli or garlic to your taste.

He gave me these quantities:

    6.4 kg (14 lb) shoulder of pork
    1.6 kg (3½ lb) rusk
    340-450 g (¾–1 lb) seasoning
    600 ml (1 pint) water

This will make about 11.4—13.6 kg (25-30 lb) of

sausages. Since this is probably more than you can use, I have scaled the recipe down as follows — which should make approximately 2.25 kg (4¹/₂ lb) sausages.

You will need

1 kg (2.2 lb) shoulder of pork, minced

225 g (8 oz) breadcrumbs or rusk

Approximately 70 g (2¹/₂ oz) seasoning, for example:

    5 g (1 tsp) salt

    1.25 g (¹/₄ tsp) pepper

    30 g (1 oz) parsley

    30 g (1 oz) sage

90 ml (3 fl oz) water

2 metres (about 6¹/₂ feet) of casing, soaked for at least an hour and washed inside and out

Method

1. Mix all the dry ingredients together.
2. Add the water and mix thoroughly.
3. Fill the casings and make links about 10 cm (4 in) long.

N.B. Alternatively, if you don't want to mess with the casings, you can make sausage patties or freeze in 450 g (1 lb) freezer bags for stuffing.

ITALIAN SAUSAGES

This recipe came about because it was impossible to find sausages seasoned in this way in the provinces. Omit the chilli flakes if you want a sweeter sausage.

Makes about 1 kg (2.2 lb) sausage

You will need

900 g (2 lb) coarsely minced pork (with some fat)

15 ml (1 tbsp) ground fennel

2 bay leaves, crumbled

15 ml (1 tbsp) dried parsley

3 cloves garlic, crushed

Pinch of dried chilli pepper flakes (optional)

5 ml (1 tsp) salt

1.25 ml ($1/4$ tsp) freshly-ground black pepper

60 ml (4 tbsp) water

Method

1. Mix all the ingredients together, set aside for an hour or two and mix again.
2. Stuff into casings, or form into patties and fry.

SAUSAGE CASSEROLE WITH POTATOES, PARPRIKA AND BASIL

You will need   Serves 2—4

450 g (1 lb) of your favourite large sausages (about 6)

750 g (1 lb 10 oz) new potatoes, scrubbed and halved

5 ml (1 tsp) paprika

Leaves from 1 sprig rosemary, chopped

Pinch of chilli powder

2 thick slices ciabatta bread, torn into pieces (optional)

Salt and freshly-ground black pepper to taste

30—45 ml (2—3 tbsp) good olive oil

120 ml (4 fl oz) full-bodied red wine

Handful of basil leaves

Method

1. Preheat the oven to 200°C (400°F/Gas Mark 6).

2. Cut the sausages in half lengthways and put them in a large roasting tin. Add the potatoes, paprika, rosemary, chilli powder, ciabatta (if using), salt and pepper and drizzle with the olive oil. Toss gently to combine.

3. Bake for 30—40 minutes, until the sausages and potatoes are cooked through. Pour the wine into the tin and cook for 5—10 minutes more, until the wine is reduced to a sticky glaze. Scatter with the basil leaves.

4. Serve with steamed broccoli, green beans or a green salad.

PASTA WITH BUTTERNUT SQUASH AND <u>SAUSAGE</u>

You will need   **Serves 4**

30 ml (2 tbsp) extra virgin olive oil, divided

450 g (1 lb) 1 pound bulk sweet Italian sausage meat
    (or normal sausage meat if you prefer)

4 cloves garlic, chopped

1 medium onion, finely chopped

1 bay leaf, fresh or dried

4—6 sprigs fresh sage leaves, sliced

250 ml (8 fl oz) dry white wine

250 ml (8 fl oz) chicken stock

225 g (8 oz) cooked butternut squash, mashed

120 ml (4 fl oz) double cream

Pinch of ground cinnamon

2.5 ml ($^1/_2$ tsp) ground or freshly-grated nutmeg

Coarse sea salt and freshly-ground black pepper

450 g (1 lb) penne pasta, cooked al dente

Romano or Parmesan cheese, for grating

Pumpernickel or whole grain bread, to serve

Method

1. Heat a large, deep non-stick frying pan over a medium high heat. Add 15 ml (1 tbsp) of the olive oil to the pan and brown the sausage. Transfer the sausage to a kitchen paper-lined plate. Drain the fat from the frying pan and return the pan to the hob. Add the remaining oil and then the garlic and onion. Sauté for 3—5 minutes until the onion is tender.
2. Add bay leaf, sage and wine to the pan. Reduce wine by half, which will take about 2 minutes. Add the stock and squash and stir to combine, stirring the sauce until it comes to the simmer. Return the

sausage to the pan, reduce the heat and stir in the cream. Season the sauce with the cinnamon and nutmeg and salt and pepper to taste. Simmer the mixture for 5–10 minutes to thicken the sauce.

3. Return the drained pasta to the pan in which you cooked it. Remove the bay leaf from the sauce and pour the sausage–squash sauce over the pasta. Toss over a low heat for 1 minute. Garnish the pasta with lots of shaved cheese and sage leaves.

4. Serve with pumpernickel or whole grain bread.

BEST EVER TOAD IN THE HOLE

This is nursery food meant for adults, but there is no reason that children will not love it also. Use the best sausages you can make or find. Serve with homemade pork gravy, onion marmalade, mustard and a tomato salad.

You will need   **Serves 4–6**

185 g (6$^{1}/_{2}$ oz) plain flour

2.5 ml ($^{1}/_{2}$ tsp) salt

Freshly-ground black pepper

15 ml (1 tbsp) fresh chopped herbs (such as sage, parsley, thyme)

3 large eggs, beaten

450 ml ($^{3}/_{4}$ pint) milk

675 g (1$^{1}/_{2}$ lb) sausages of your choice

45 ml (3 tbsp) beef dripping, lard or cooking oil

Method

1. Mix the flour, salt, pepper and herbs in a large bowl. Make a well in the centre and add the eggs. Whisk in the milk with an electric whisk.

2. Leave the batter to stand while you cook the sausages.

3. Heat the oven to 220°C (450°F/Gas Mark 7).

4. Heat the dripping, lard or cooking oil in a roasting tin, add the sausages and bake for 10 minutes or so until just cooked.

5. Whisk the batter again.

6. Remove the tin from the oven and place on the hob over a high heat until the fat starts to smoke. Pour the batter into the tin and put back in the oven. Be careful because the fat may spit.

7. Bake for 25–30 minutes until the batter has risen dramatically and is golden. Cut into portions and serve immediately.

HONEY ROAST HAM

If you use a gammon on the bone you will have the makings for soup, but I have found a D-shape boned joint much easier to work with. I prefer to soak my hams for at least 8 hours before putting them in the oven because even unsmoked gammon can be a bit too salty for me, but this is a matter of taste.

You will need   **Serves 8–10**

2 kg (4 1/2 lb) joint unsmoked gammon

30 ml (2 tbsp) runny honey

30 ml (2 tbsp) sherry or medium-dry white wine

15 ml (1 tbsp) soft brown sugar

5 ml (1 tsp) Dijon mustard

Method

1. Heat the oven to 180°C (350°F/Gas Mark 4).

2. Line a large roasting tin with a robust sheet of

aluminium foil large enough to cover the gammon.

3. If you have soaked the ham, dry it with kitchen paper. Weigh it to calculate the cooking time if you have not already done so. Put it on a metal rack and place into the tin. Bring the foil up around the ham and scrunch the edges together to enclose the meat, not wrapping it too tightly. Insert an oven thermometer to check for doneness.

4. Calculate the cooking time (about 45 minutes per kg/20 minutes per pound). When your oven thermometer (or an instant-read thermometer) registers 60°C (140°F) internal temperature, remove the meat from the oven and increase the oven to 200°C (400°F/Gas Mark 6).

5. Peel back the foil, but do not remove it. Cut the rind and string from the gammon, leaving the fat. Score the fat in a diamond pattern with a sharp knife.

6. Mix the honey, sherry or wine, sugar and mustard together and spoon or paint over the meat with a pastry brush. Protect the sides of the meat with the foil, leaving the top uncovered.

7. Bake for 20–30 minutes, basting with the pan juices a couple of times until golden brown and the internal temperature of the meat measures 66°C (150°F). Remove from the oven, cool slightly and carve in thick slices. You may want to save the meat juices in the tin to make sauce.

ESPRESSO CHILLI GLAZED HAM

For this recipe use a fully cooked smoked ham, preferably wood smoked with no water added. Trim off the outside layer of fat and skin all the way to the pink meat, so when you're ready to carve you don't cut away the flavourful glaze.

You will need   **Makes 16 or more servings**

 Half a fully cooked smoked ham (about 3.6 kg/8 lb)

 900 ml (1^1/$_2$ pints) fresh orange juice

 15 ml (1 tbsp) grated orange rind

 200 g (7 oz) brown sugar

 250 ml (8 fl oz) Kahlua or other coffee-flavoured liqueur

 15 ml (1 tbsp) Chinese chilli paste with garlic,
   or sambal olek

 2.5 ml (^{1}/$_2$ tsp) freshly-ground black pepper

 60 ml (4 tbsp) brewed espresso or 15 ml (1 tbsp) instant
   espresso powder

Method

1. Preheat the oven to 160°C (325°F/Gas Mark 3).

2. Cut the thick layer of fat and skin from the ham and discard. Place the ham in a roasting tin. (For easier clean up, line the pan with aluminium foil because the glaze will drip off and burn.) Roast the ham for 1 hour.

3. While the ham is roasting, make the glaze. Combine the orange juice and rind, brown sugar, Kahlua, chilli paste and pepper in a large saucepan. Bring to the boil over a high heat, then reduce the heat to medium and simmer the mixture until it is reduced by about half and is as thick as maple syrup, for about 35 minutes.

4. Whisk in the espresso or espresso powder. You should have about 450 ml (³/₄ pint) of glaze. You are going to use half this amount to brush the ham while it is roasting, and reserve the other half for brushing on the ham after it is sliced.

5. After the first hour of cooking, brush the ham with the glaze. Roast for another hour, brushing with the glaze every 15 minutes. Since the ham is already cooked, you just need to warm it all the way through. Check for an internal temperature of 54–60°C (130–140°F) using an instant-read meat thermometer. Remove the ham from the oven when it is nicely browned and warmed through.

6. To serve, slice the ham and brush the slices with the remaining glaze.

Source: Marshall Field & Company, Chicago, Illinois

HAM AND POTATOES AU GRATIN

If ham and cheese is a beloved combination (and who can argue with the truth of that statement?) then it figures that ham would certainly go well in potatoes au gratin — and you'll see that it does when you try this recipe that utilises your leftover Christmas ham.

You will need   **Serves 6**

    4 medium to large potatoes

    225 g (8 oz) cooked ham, diced small or shredded

    65 g (2¹/₂ oz) butter or margarine

    1 medium to large onion, chopped

    salt, to taste, but sparingly (because the ham typically
       will be salty)

Freshly-ground pepper and garlic powder to taste,
 used liberally

15 ml (1 tbsp) plain flour

475 ml (16 fl oz) milk

350 g (12 oz) grated Cheddar cheese

25 g (1 oz) breadcrumbs

Method

1. Preheat the oven to 160°C (325°F/Gas Mark 3. Peel the potatoes and cut into thin slices, starting at one end so the slices form rough circles.

2. Layer a casserole dish with the potatoes, forming as many layers as it takes to use them all. Sprinkle the ham bits evenly among the layers of potatoes.

3. In a large frying pan over a medium-high heat, melt the butter or margarine and sauté the onions until they are soft and translucent. As they cook, add the salt, pepper, and garlic powder. When the onions are soft, add the flour and stir for a couple of minutes. The mixture should start to thicken. Add the milk and two-thirds of the cheese, and bring to the slow boil, adjusting the heat as needed and stirring frequently. Allow to boil for 2 minutes, then pour the sauce over the potatoes and ham in the casserole.

4. Put the casserole in the oven, uncovered, and bake for 80 minutes. Remove from the oven and sprinkle the remaining cheese and breadcrumbs on top. Return to the oven for another 30 minutes.

Recipe by Cynthia MacGregor,
www.cynthiamacgregor.com

SUSIE'S HAM LOAF

For many years now our friend and my in-law, Susie in Florida, has made this ham loaf, which she serves with cheese grits for Christmas Eve supper. I have seen several similar recipes that have an Amish provenance. You can mince the ham and the pork in your food processor with good results. I usually do it separately and then mix together.

You will need   Serves 6–8

450 g (1 lb) minced ham
675 g (1½ lb) minced pork
115 g (4 oz) fresh white breadcrumbs
3 eggs, beaten
Salt and freshly-ground black pepper
175 ml (6 fl oz) milk
Juice of 1 lemon
5 ml (1 tsp) American mustard
225 g (8 oz) soft dark brown sugar (see below)

Method

1. Preheat the oven to 180°C (350°F/Gas Mark 4).
2. Mix the ham, pork, breadcrumbs, eggs, salt and pepper and milk, lemon juice and mustard together in a large bowl with your clean hands. Form into a loaf and place on a greased baking sheet or pack into a large loaf tin (a 900 g/2 lb tin may not be large enough, but be creative). During the last half an hour glaze with the lemon, mustard and sugar.
3. Bake the meatloaf for 1½ hours. Remove from the oven and let sit for a minute or five to let the juices settle. You could serve this with a cheesy polenta, which is the closest I can come to grits in the UK.

N.B. This may be too sweet for British palates. You might want to halve the amount of sugar and mix it with 60 ml (4 tbsp) cider vinegar and 120 ml (4 fl oz) dry white wine or water and a spoonful of mustard powder for a bit of a bite.

IRISH CRUBEEENS (CRUNCHY PIGS' TROTTERS)

Throughout the 19th century and halfway into the 20th, these finger-licking good snacks were offered in Irish pubs (probably to sell more stout) or in street stalls located near pubs. They became less popular as the population craved more exotic fare and turned up their noses at these rustic specialities.

For a number of years now, these and other inexpensive parts of the pig have not been used in our normal cooking; often only encountered in celebrity chefs' restaurants or magazine articles in the UK. But they are now enjoying a renaissance. Even if you don't have a butcher who is featuring these items, one of the posh supermarkets is now introducing pigs' trotters to its shelves. If you would like to try a real old-fashioned treat, this recipe is Irish in origin.

You will need   **Serves 4**

8 fresh pigs' feet, ideally the front ones

2 large onions

2 large carrots

2 bay leaves

Bunch of parsley

12 peppercorns

1 egg, beaten

115 g (4 oz) dried breadcrumbs

Bacon fat or oil for roasting

Parsley to garnish

Soda bread and stout to serve

Method

1. Wash the pigs' feet well. Put into a large pot with the onions, carrots, bay leaves, parsley and peppercorns; cover with cold water and bring to the boil. Cover, reduce the heat, and simmer gently for 2—3 hours, until the meat is very tender.

2. Remove the trotters carefully from the cooking liquid. (They may try to fall apart if they're tender enough. This is a good sign, but can make it a bit messy.) Drain and pat dry with kitchen paper. When slightly cooled, dip in the beaten egg, then roll in breadcrumbs.

3. Preheat the oven to 220°C (450F/Gas Mark 8). Heat the bacon fat or oil in a shallow roasting dish. Place the trotters in the dish and spoon the fat or oil over them. Roast in the oven for 15-30 minutes until crisp and golden. Garnish with the parsley and serve immediately with soda bread and stout.

CHILLI-BARBECUED BELLY PORK WITH SWEET POTATOES

Another formerly very inexpensive cut of pork has come back into the spotlight and is the signature dish of many chefs. Yet it is easy enough to prepare at home.

You will need   Serves 4

675 g (24 oz) passata with garlic and onion

10 g (2 tsp) chilli paste

45 ml (3 tbsp) cider vinegar

75 g (2^1/$_2$ oz) light brown soft sugar

30 g (2 tbsp) tomato ketchup

675 g (1^1/$_2$ lb) pork belly, cut into 4 slices

1 kg (2.2 lb) sweet potatoes, scrubbed and peeled (about 4 medium)

30 ml (2 tbsp) mild olive oil

10 ml (2 tsp) Cajun seasoning

Method

1. Put the passata, chilli paste, vinegar, sugar and tomato ketchup into a medium saucepan and bring to the boil over a medium heat. Simmer for 5 minutes until the sugar dissolves.

2. Preheat the oven to 190°C (375°F/Gas Mark 5).

3. Roll up the pork slices and secure each with metal skewers. Place in a shallow ovenproof dish and pour the sauce over. Turn to coat. Cover the dish with aluminium foil, cook in the oven for 20 minutes, then turn over and cook for a further 25 minutes.

4. Meanwhile, cut each sweet potato into 8 long wedges and place in a roasting tin. Mix the oil and

Cajun seasoning together, drizzle over the potatoes and toss well to coat completely. Cook in the oven for 25-30 minutes, turning once, until the potatoes are tender when pierced with a fork.

5. Place the pork slices under a preheated hot grill and cook for 5 minutes on each side, basting with the sauce, until golden and crisp. Remove the skewers and serve with the sweet potato wedges and a fresh green salad.

SLOW-ROASTED BELLY PORK WITH CREAMY MASH AND SPINACH

You will need   Serves 4

    500g (1 lb 2 oz) piece pork belly

    Pork or chicken stock

    Sautéed spinach, to serve

For the marinade:

    240 ml (8 fl oz) soy sauce

    240 ml (8 fl oz) port wine

    240 ml (8 fl oz) red wine

    140 g (5 oz) brown sugar

    100 ml ($3^{1}/_{2}$ fl oz) sherry wine

    4 coriander seeds

    4 peppercorns

    2 bay leaves

    30 g (1 oz) fresh thyme leaves

    2 star anise

    140 g (5 oz) mild honey

    3 onions, chopped

    2 carrots,chopped

    1 leek, chopped

    2 sticks celery, chopped

For the creamy mash:

750g even-sized Maris Piper or King Edward potatoes, scrubbed

60 ml (2 fl oz) milk

60 ml (2 fl oz) double cream

115 g (4 oz) butter

Salt and freshly-ground black pepper

Method

1. Preheat the oven to 180°C (350°F/Gas Mark 4).

2. Combine all the marinade ingredients in a large saucepan and bring to the boil. Boil until the liquid is reduced by half, then remove from the heat and allow to cool.

3. Heat a large flameproof baking dish on the hob until hot and brown the pork belly all over for about 3 minutes. Remove from the heat.

4. Pour the marinade over the pork belly, rubbing it well into the meat, then pour in enough pork or chicken stock to cover. Slowly bake the pork belly for about 2 hours until very tender.

5. When cooked, remove the pork from the cooking liquid, divide it into serving portions and keep warm.

6. Strain the cooking liquid into a saucepan and cook until it is reduced to a glaze.

7. *Make the mash:* put the potatoes into a pan of salted water and bring to the boil. Reduce the heat and simmer for 20–25 minutes until they are tender when pierced with a small knife. Drain well.

8. Peel the skins off the potatoes using a small paring knife, then mash them.

9. Melt the butter and add to the mash. Heat the milk and cream together and add to the mash,

whisking until smooth. Season with salt and freshly ground black pepper.

10. Serve the marinated pork belly over the creamy mash, topped with a bit of the reduced glaze, accompanied by a mound of sautéed spinach.

MEXICAN CHILLI RUB

This is a wonderful mole-like spice mix with a hint of a chocolate flavour. It is wonderful on pork, turkey and chicken.

You will need   **Makes about 55 g (2 oz)**

   15 ml (1 tbsp) chilli powder

   15 ml (1 tbsp) paprika

   10 ml (2 tsp) ground cumin

   5 ml (1 tsp) freshly-ground black pepper

   5 ml (1 tsp) dried oregano

   5 ml (1 tsp) unsweetened cocoa powder

   7.5 ml (1½ tsp) dark brown sugar

   5 ml (1 tsp) granulated sugar

   5 ml (1 tsp) coarse sea salt

Method

Combine all ingredients in a small bowl and mix to blend. You can store this in a glass jar in a cool, dry place away from the light for up to three months.

PIG
MISCELLANY

NON-CULINARY PRODUCTS
FROM THE PIG

Not only do pigs provide us with wonderful food, other products to enhance our lives are also obtained from them.

Parts of the pig are used in hundreds of medical products, for example, insulin, or for replacement heart valves. There are two types of replacement valves, mechanical or biological. Biological valves are valves of animals, like pigs, which undergo several chemical procedures in order to make them suitable for implantation in the human heart. The porcine (pig) heart is most similar to the human heart, and therefore represents the best anatomical fit for replacement.

Lord Winston, the UK fertility expert, is to start breeding pigs in order to produce hearts, livers and kidneys for transplanting in humans. Winston believes genetically modified organs provide the best solution to tackle the current shortage of human organs. A record number of almost 8000 British patients are waiting for an organ.

The highly controversial method of transplanting animal organs — xenotransplantation — has been tried before with limited success. Many of the organs were rejected by the patients' immune system. The pigs will be bred with approximately six human genes to prevent patients rejecting their organs. Winston's team will need to prove that the pig organs can be sufficiently modified to survive long-term in the human body.

Winston said, 'Pigs' organs are the right size for human transplantation, and they work similarly to human organs. Of course this raises a moral problem, but it is much more ethical to use a pig to save a human life than to use it for relatively unnecessary meat eating.'

Pigs involved in experiments have successfully produced transgenic sperm, but Winston acknowledges that British and European laws prevent the team from using the pigs to mate.

The research project is now moving from Britain to America after British regulations and a shortage of funding prevented experiments here, with the pig breeding to take place in Missouri. This method could see hundreds of genetically modified pigs reared simultaneously for their organs which could be taken from pigs as young as one year.

There are some more mundane, but excellent, products provided by our porcine friends. Pigs have a firm, thick skin covered with a usually sparse coat of stiff hairs called bristles. Pigskin is renowned for producing a high-quality leather that 'breathes' better than other types of leather. This is because only pigskin has bristle follicles that extend completely through the hide. Pigskin is used traditionally for gloves, luggage, belts, jackets and shoes.

Pig hair (usually boar) provides durable bristles for brushes.

Our grandmothers believed that lard (pig fat) soap was terrific for use as a laundry product to remove stains from clothing. Apparently, people are still making soap out of lard for those reasons, plus it is gentle enough to use on the skin.

Pigskin is also the name used for an American or Canadian football, due to the early method of using a pig's bladder to cover the ball.

PIGS IN HISTORY

Few animals have such economic importance to mankind yet suffer from such an appalling image as does the pig. As a domestic animal it is a source of a wide variety of meat products, high-quality leather, durable bristles for many kinds of brushes and hundreds of medical items. At the same time, the pig is frequently regarded as unclean and even untouchable by many people.

All pigs belong to the family *Suidae* and the order *Artidactyla* (even-toed, hoofed animals). In addition to the domestic species, several types of wild pigs are found on the Eurasian and African continents. The Eurasian wild boar (*Sus scrofa*), a popular game animal during medieval times, still roams over many parts of Europe, Asia, and North Africa. The pygmy hog (*S. salvanius*), the smallest of the wild pigs, is found in Nepal and northern India; it is now threatened with extinction. The warty pig (*S. verrucosus*) and the bearded pig (*S. barbatus*) live in parts of Southeast Asia, Malaysia, and the Philippines. The babirusa (*Babyrousa babyrussa*) lives in regions of Indonesia. Areas in Africa, south of the Sahara, are home to the warthog (*Phacochoerus aethiopicus*), the giant forest pig (*Hylochoerus meinertzhageni*), and the bush pig (*Potamochoerus porcus*). Large numbers of feral pigs (pigs who have escaped domestication to live in the wild) are found on every continent except Antarctica. Wild pigs roam forests, meadows and swamps. They are surefooted and rapid runners, good swimmers and fond of mud baths.

When cornered they will fight courageously and will use their tusks as weapons. They are mainly active at night and have an omnivorous diet of fungi, roots, bulbs, tubers, fruit, snails, earthworms, reptiles, young birds, eggs, small rodents and carrion.

In spite of their reputation, pigs are neither filthy nor stupid. Because their sweat glands are relatively ineffective in lowering body temperature, pigs seek relief from the heat by wallowing in mud or shallow waterholes. When provided with a clean environment sheltered from the sun, however, pigs are fastidious. Furthermore, in tests of intelligence, pigs have proved to be among the smartest of all domestic animals; even more intelligent than dogs.

Pigs are closely related to peccaries (a small mammal with a superficial resemblance to a pig) and distantly related to hippopotamuses. Their snouts end in a flat, rounded disk, which is used by most species to root for food. Both males and females have tusks, which they use for defence. The tusks are sharpened as the pig chews; its upper and lower tusks rub against one another.

The pig has existed for at least 45 million years as a stocky, round-bodied, flat-snouted creature. They come in all sizes, from the small pygmy to the giant forest hog. But the domestic pig can be much heavier than those in the wild.

The first domestication of the pig is thought to

have taken place in China around 4900 BC and may have occurred as early as 10,000 BC in Thailand. Many breeds were developed especially in Europe and they became important farm animals. Their average lifespan in the wild is 15—20 years but may be up to 27 years. Litter size varies from 2—12 piglets. Domestic pigs have much larger litters with one of 37 recorded. Hair varies from very bristly and practically hairless to the curly woolly coats of the Mangalitzas.

The pig has a long history of connection with humans. Unlike horses, mules, and oxen, they could not pull our ploughs or carts. They gave us neither milk to drink nor wool to spin into clothing. They were of value to us for only one thing: food. Pork is rich in protein, fat, niacin, zinc, phosphorus, and other minerals. In times of great cold, the meat from pigs helped our forebears survive. Thus, pigs were revered for the precious gift of their lives. They were honoured in seasonal rituals for the help they gave our ancestors to survive, who in turn raised them from piglets and often loved them as pets.

Recent studies of pig DNA reveal that instead of being domesticated only from wild boars in the Near East and Asia, as was previously thought, and then slowly spreading worldwide through human trade and migration, pigs were tamed from local wild relatives in several different locations. Although the original species of wild boar originated among the islands of Southeast Asia, our first evidence for domestication dates back 9000 years to eastern Turkey — and some centuries later to China. Since we have no approximate dates for other regions, experts do not know if techniques for taming wild pigs spread by word of mouth, or if the idea arose independently. There is firm evidence, however, pointing to further Neolithic (later Stone Age) domestication arising independently in Italy, Central Europe, Northern India, the Southeast Asian mainland and the islands of Southeast Asia.

Pigs in Neolithic Britain were an early domesticated variety that gave birth only once a year in the spring. In 2005, as part of a 10-year archeological investigation of the Stonehenge site, scientific analysis of pigs' teeth from Durrington Walls (a ceremonial site near Stonehenge), revealed that the teeth came from pigs who were about nine months old when they were sacrificed, suggesting that this took place in midwinter and the large number of pig bones indicate that this was a major regional festival. The teeth were also decayed, leading to speculation that the pigs were deliberately fed honey to sweeten their meat.

PIGS IN LITERATURE

Pigs are the most represented of all barnyard animals in literature. The shy defencelessness and goodness of Wilbur, the pig in *Charlotte's Web*, is why Charlotte spins words into her webs and saves him from death.

This book begins when John Arable's sow gives birth to a litter of piglets, and Mr Arable discovers one of them is a runt and decides to kill it. However, his eight year old daughter Fern begs him to let it live. Her father gives it to her as a pet and she names the piglet Wilbur.

Wilbur is hyperactive; always exploring new things. He lives with Fern for a few weeks and then is sold to her uncle, Homer Zuckerman. Although Fern visits him at the farm as often as she can, Wilbur gets lonelier day after day. Eventually, a warm and soothing voice tells him that she is going to be his friend. The next day, he wakes up and meets his new friend: Charlotte, the grey spider. Wilbur soon becomes a member of the community of animals who live in the cellar of Zuckerman's barn. When the old sheep in the barn cellar tells Wilbur that he is going to be killed and eaten at Christmas, he turns to Charlotte for help. Charlotte has the idea of writing words in her web extolling Wilbur's excellence, reasoning that if she can make Wilbur sufficiently famous, he will not be killed. Thanks to Charlotte's efforts, Wilbur not only lives, but goes to the county fair with Charlotte and wins a prize.

Porky Pig, the first animated cartoon character in Warner Bros. *Looney Tunes* series, was created by the studio and proved very popular. Even after he was supplanted by later characters, Porky continued to be well-liked by moviegoers and, more importantly, the Warners' directors, who recast him in numerous everyman and sidekick roles. He is known for his signature line at the end of each short, 'Th-th-th-that's all folks!' The slogan had also been used by both Bosko and Buddy and even Beans at the end of every *Looney Tunes* cartoon.

The *Three Little Pigs* fairy tale gave us one pig-hero who is industrious and clever as opposed as his two careless brothers.

The words for the Mother Goose counting rhyme *This Little Piggy* are used to point out each one of a child's toes, starting with the big toe:

This little piggy went to market
This little piggy stayed home
This little piggy had roast beef
This little piggy had none
And this little piggy went wee wee wee
   all the way home

The last line is used to accompany the child being tickled by the person saying it. It is extremely popular and has been passed from generation to generation, the first publication date being 1728.

Piglet is a fictional character from A. A. Milne's

Winnie The Pooh books. Piglet is a baby pig who is the best friend of Winnie the Pooh. Despite the fact that he is a 'Very Small Animal' with a generally timid disposition, he often conquers his fears and seems to want to be brave.

The Sheep-Pig is a novel by Dick King-Smith. It was first published in 1983. The book is set in rural England, where King-Smith spent 20 years as a farmer. The book won the Guardian Children's Fiction Award in 1984. It took film producer and co-writer George Miller 10 years to take the book from paperback to the big screen, when in 1995, it charmed the world as *Babe*.

The plot revolves around a young pig, won at a fair by a local farmer, Mr Hoggett. Mr Hoggett keeps a sheep farm and has no use for pigs, so his wife intends to fatten up the little porker for Christmas dinner.

In unfamiliar surroundings the little piglet is scared and Fly, one of the farm's two sheep dogs, takes pity on him and comforts him. She asks what his name is, and he replies that his mother called all her children Babe. Fly and her puppies teach Babe the rules of the farm, including that only dogs and cats are allowed in the house. From the beginning, the pig makes friends with the other animals on the farm, even though they are reluctant to be friendly to an animal they know is destined to die.

One day, while the sheep dogs and their puppies are in the fields with Farmer Hoggett, Babe meets an elderly ewe, named Ma. Babe decides to visit Ma and heads up to the paddocks. He arrives as sheep rustlers are stealing the sheep. Babe protects the sheep as best he can, even biting one of the rustler's dogs, and making such a terrible noise that Farmer Hoggett hears it and drives to investigate. On hearing the farmer coming, the rustlers drive away, with few sheep. Babe has saved most of the flock and as a reward, one day Farmer Hoggett takes Babe with him up to the sheep fields and, on a whim, asks the pig to round up the sheep. Babe at first fails to do this, because he is trying to be aggressive like a sheep dog. Ma appears in the centre of the herd and tells him that all a polite little pig like him has to do is ask. To Farmer Hoggett's astonishment, the sheep obey by walking in perfect straight lines around their pen. From then on, Babe accompanies Farmer Hoggett up to the sheep fields every day.

The *Muppet Show*'s Miss Piggy has an 'attitude' that delights us all. Miss Piggy began as a minor character in *The Muppet Show* TV series, but gradually developed into one of the central characters of the show; she did not appear in the earlier *Sesame Street*. Miss Piggy is convinced she is destined for stardom, and nothing is going to stand in her way. She presents a public face of the soul of feminine charm, but can instantly fly into a violent rage whenever she thinks she's insulted or thwarted. These pigs charm us with their antics and also teach us about our own humanity.

Less lovable, but every bit as important, are the

pigs in George Orwell's *Animal Farm*. Power corrupts, but absolute power corrupts absolutely and this is vividly and eloquently proved in Orwell's short novel. *Animal Farm* is a simple fable of great symbolic value, and as Orwell himself explained: 'it is the history of a revolution that went wrong'. The novel can be seen as the historical analysis of the causes of the failure of communism, or as a mere fairy tale; in any case it tells a good story that aims to prove that human nature and diversity prevent people from being equal and happy, or at least equally happy. *Animal Farm* tells the simple and tragic story of what happens when the oppressed farm animals rebel, drive out Mr Jones, the farmer, and attempt to rule the farm themselves, on an equal basis. What the animals seem to have aimed at was a utopian sort of communism, where each would work according to his capacity, respecting the needs of others. The venture failed, and *Animal Farm* ended up being a dictatorship of pigs, who were the brightest and most idle of the animals.

These are only a few of the currently well-known pigs in literature, included to indicate how beloved, intelligent and well-thought of they are by both children and adults.

PIGS IN RELIGION

WHY DON'T JEWS AND MUSLIMS EAT PORK?

Swine are considered non-kosher ('unfit' or 'unclean') in Judaism and haraam ('forbidden') in Islam.

For the Jews, the pig is an unclean animal and its flesh may not be eaten nor its carcass touched. In ancient times, Jews did not hesitate to risk their lives for their devotion to the Torah in this regard; in the middle of the second century BC, they stood against the Seleucid King Antiochus IV when he defiled the Temple of Jerusalem by dedicating it to Olympian Zeus, immolating pigs and other unclean animals and offering them in sacrifice.

The dietary prohibition of the Torah is pre-Israelite in origin, for abstinence from the meat of the pig was a widespread, religiously motivated custom that is well attested among the Phoenicians, the Cypriots, the Syrians, the Arabs, and in fact among all Semitic peoples with the exception of the Babylonians. Although its religious origins have sunk into oblivion, the custom has been preserved: Jews and Muslims of today abstain from eating pork in accordance with its strict prohibition by the Torah and the Qur'an.

One explanation is that trichinosis, leprosy and other diseases harboured by pigs were rampant in ancient cultures. These diseases were not well understood, but a way they could deal with it was to forbid the consumption of pork.

Another possibility, according to Wikipedia:

> 'Pigs require water and shade woods with seeds, but those conditions are scarce in Israel and Arabia. They cannot forage grass like ruminants. Instead, they compete with humans for expensive grain.'

PIG TALES

This little piggy ruled the earth long before dinosaurs — (abstracted from *The Sunday Times* 9 September 2008)

Paleontologists have discovered a Porcine Age, when pig-like creatures ruled the earth. The animals, known as *lystrosaurs* were among the only survivors of the greatest mass extinction event the world has seen when, around 251 million years ago, 95% of all living species were wiped out by a series of volcanic eruptions.

The eruptions eliminated every large predator, so for a million years or more the lystrosaurs had the planet — and all of its succulent plant life — almost entirely to themselves.

'They fed and spread. We think there were billions of them,' said Paul Wignall, professor of paleo-environment at Leeds University. 'Their fossils are everywhere.'

Reconstructions from fossils suggest they were similar in size and stature to modern pigs, complete with snouts and small tusks for rooting around in vegetation.

Trapped pig pulled out of drain
21 August 2008 (Story from *BBC News*)

A pig had to be rescued by firefighters after getting stuck in a drain near a Hampshire river.

Crews were called to Fairthorne Manor in Botley Road, Curbridge, where the pig became lodged down the drain near the banks of the River Hamble.

Working with a vet, RSPCA officer, the firefighters and a rural safety officer, the five-year-old animal was eventually extracted from the drain.

The pig, a Gloucester Old Spot and Middle White cross, was unhurt.

Jim Green, Hampshire Fire and Rescue Service's rural safety officer, said: 'It was important for us to get the animal out as quickly as possible as she was quite stressed by the experience. Working together we dug around the animal, removing brickwork until we were able to put a five-metre strap around her. Then we were able to pull the pig out using manpower before she was checked over by a vet and given some fresh water to drink.'

Pigs in clover
July 2008 (from *People Like Them, Sunday Times*)

You are nobody in Somerset these days without your own pair of rare breed porkers. The hotelier Martin Miller — famed host of late-night jamming sessions featuring Kate Moss, Jimmy Page and Slash — is building a castle with a crystal chandelier for his two best boys, Boris and Johnson, at his new place, Glencot House.

This little piggy wore wellies . . .
June 2008, Bedale, North Yorkshire: Cinders, a six-week old piglet became famous when she hit the news because she was believed to be suffering from mysophobia — fear of contact with dirt. This is a big problem when you live in a pigsty.

Farmers Debbie and Andrew Keeble were baffled when the Saddleback piglet refused to get her feet dirty. She just stood in a corner shaking while her brothers and sisters romped in the mud. But the farmers noticed that if she was moved to a dry patch, she was perfectly happy. So they asked a designer friend to create bespoke wellies, which have been made with no footwell, allowing her trotters to slip straight in. The wellies did the trick. Now the couple, who run an award-winning sausage company, have chosen Cinders as the face of a campaign to highlight the plight of the UK's struggling pig farmers.

The Tamworth Two
January, 1998. There was a lot of excitement in the town where I live when a pair of Tamworth pigs escaped while being unloaded from a lorry at an abbatoir in Malmesbury, Wiltshire. The agile pair, later named Butch and Sundance (after *Butch Cassidy and the Sundance Kid*) went 'on the run', chased by an army of abattoir workers, police and news reporters. Their dramatic escape from the abattoir just before being slaughtered, and their wily tricks to evade capture, attracted media attention and stole the hearts of the animal-loving British nation.

The intrepid porcines squeezed under a supposedly secure fence and swam a large icy river in their bid for freedom — swine are naturally strong swimmers.

Even when they were finally discovered, six days after escaping, one of the young boars continued to evade capture for a further 36 hours in a confrontation with an army of animal handlers, RSPCA humane society officers, abattoir staff, police, dogs and a tempting female Tamworth sow. He even survived the first two of three immobilising darts before finally succumbing.

The pigs were eventually found on January 15th in the garden of local residents — only a quarter of a mile away from the abattoir. They had been feeding regularly on kitchen vegetable waste.

A local butcher voiced the widespread opinion that it would be 'unsporting' to kill the two swine after such a daring bid to avoid the fate which befell their less-fleet-of-foot companion, who had been unloaded at the same time.

A national newspaper arranged for them to be re-homed in an animal sanctuary — prompting headlines about how the intrepid swine had managed to 'Save their Bacon'!

The BBC made a 60-minute film about their adventure called *The Legend of the Tamworth Two*, in 2003.

Swindon, Wiltshire

Swindon began as a Saxon village. The original Old English name was swin dun, meaning 'swine down', or hill that was a pasture for pigs. Some early records refer to it as Higheswindon or Swyndon super montem (= Swindon on the hill). *The Domesday Book* of 1086 calls it Suindune. One of the local newspapers said that, at one time, there were more pigs than people in Swindon.

Pig Olympics

The Pig Olympics are a sporting event organised for specially-bred and trained piglets.

The 2006 competition was held in Moscow, Russia, while in 2005 the Pig Olympics were held in China. The last Pig Olympics was in 2009.

Events within the competition include pig racing (over an obstacle course), pig swimming (introduced at the 2006 Pig Olympics), and 'pigball' or 'swineball' which is much like football or soccer.

The piglets in the games are not eaten; instead, they are bred for the next generation of pig-players.

CHINESE ASTROLOGY: THE YEAR OF THE PIG

1923, 1935, 1947, 1959, 1971, 1983, 1995, 2007

People born in the Year of the Pig are chivalrous and gallant. Whatever they do, they do with all their strength. For Boar Year people, there is no left or right, and there is no retreat. They have tremendous fortitude and great honesty. They don't make many friends, but they make them for life, and anyone having a Boar Year friend is fortunate for they are extremely loyal. They don't talk much, but have a great thirst for knowledge. They study a great deal and are generally well informed. Boar people are quick tempered, yet they hate arguments and quarreling. They are kind to their loved ones. No matter how bad problems seem to be, Boar people try to work them out, honestly if sometimes impulsively. They are most compatible with Rabbits and Sheep.

2007 was supposedly a particularly auspicious year because the Chinese Zodiac says that the Year of the Golden Pig comes only once every 600 years and rumour has it, 2007 was this special year. It is Golden because the combination of elemental Fire, the sign Pig and Yin/Yang components bring this year once every six centuries!

It is said that children born under this sign will live in comfort as wealth and luck are always near.

PIG EXPRESSIONS

The English language is peppered with expressions using the words 'pig', 'hog', 'swine', 'pork', 'bacon' and 'sow'. Some of them have quite interesting origins. Here are a few of the most popular ones.

Piggy bank

Why do we save our coins in a piggy bank? Because someone made a mistake. During the Middle Ages, circa 15th century, metal was expensive and seldom used for household wares. Instead, dishes and pots were made from an economical clay called pygg. Whenever housewives could save an extra coin, they dropped it into one of their clay jars. They called this their pygg bank or their pyggy bank.

Over the next 200–300 years, people forgot the the word 'pygg' referred to the earthenware material. In the 19th century when English potters received requests for pyggy banks, they produced banks shaped like a pig. These pigs appealed to the customers and delighted their children.

Piggyback

Children usually love being given piggyback rides. When you give a child a piggyback ride, what you normally do is to put him on your shoulders or on your back and walk around with him. The expression 'piggyback' comes from 'pick a pack'. In the old days — and I guess even now — it was common practice for individuals who had to carry a heavy object to invariably place it on their back.

This method of carrying things around was called 'pick a pack'. And `pick a pack' when said quickly became `pickapack'. Parents often carried their children 'pickapack' too. But children, because they loved animals so much changed 'pickapack' to 'piggyback'.

In a pig's eye
Under no circumstances.

Pig in a poke
Something that is offered in a manner that conceals its true nature or value.

Pig in the middle
A person who is placed in an awkward position between two others (after a children's playground ball game for three with one in the middle).

Pig iron
Crude iron from a smelting furnace. This is a mere play upon the word 'sow'. When iron is melted, it runs off into a channel called a sow, the lateral branches of which are called the 'pigs'. Here the iron cools and is called pig iron.

Pig Latin
A made-up jargon in which the first letter of a word is pronounced last with -ay. So what did you do today? would become Hatway idday ouyay oday odaytay?

Pigs might fly
An expression of disbelief; something that you say

which means you think there is no chance at all of something happening.

Pigging out
To eat ravenously.

Lipstick on a pig
When Barack Obama told a crowd at a campaign event in September 2008 'You can put lipstick on a pig, but it's still a pig', the McCain campaign swiftly took offence, claiming the analogy was directed at vice-presidential nominee Sarah Palin. Obama campaign spokeswoman Jen Psaki countered the accusation, saying, 'That expression is older than my grandfather's grandfather and it means that you can dress something up, but it doesn't change what it is.'

Make a pig's ear of
Make a mess of, bungle.

Hog heaven
A state of utter bliss or contentment.

Saving your bacon
If something saves your bacon, it saves your life or rescues you from a desperate situation.

Ham it up
To show expressions or emotions in an over the top manner.

Pork pie hat
A pork pie hat is a men's dress hat that resembles

a fedora, but has a thinner brim and a short, flat-topped, round crown with an indentation all the way around. Most pork pie hats are felt, but straw styles also exist.

The pork pie hat originated in the mid-19th century, when it was commonly worn by American cowboys before the stetson hat became popular. However, the term originally referred to a women's style of the same era. The pork pie hat is so named because its shape resembles a pork pie.

Porky
Short for porky pies, Cockney slang for 'lies'. 'Don't be telling me porkies!' which, translated, means 'Don't tell me lies!'

Go the whole hog
To do something as entirely or completely as possible; to reserve or hold back nothing.

Casting pearls before swine
Pearls before swine refers to a quotation from the discourse on holiness, a section of Jesus Christ's Sermon on the Mount:

> 'Do not give what is holy to dogs, and do not throw pearls before swine, lest they trample them under their feet, and turn and tear you to pieces.' (Matthew 7:6). The meaning is pretty simple to figure out: 'Do not persist in offering what is sacred or of value to those who have no appreciation for it, because your gift will not only become contaminated and be

despised, your generous efforts could also be rebuffed and perhaps even openly attacked.'

Make a silk purse out of a sow's ear

Being able to turn something ugly or inferior into something attractive or of value. Massachusetts industrialist Arthur D. Little liked a challenge. In 1921, after hearing someone quote Jonathan Swift's adage, 'You can't make a silk purse of a sow's ear', Little decided to try to do just that. From a meat-packer he obtained a form of glue made from the skin and gristle of sows' ears. Taking an amount roughly equivalent to one sow's ear, he had it filtered and forced through a spinneret into a mixture of formaldehyde and acetone. The glue emerged as 16 fine, colourless streams that hardened and then combined to form a single composite fibre. Little soaked the fibre in dyed glycerine. Then he wove the resulting thread into cloth on a handloom and fashioned the cloth into an elegant purse; the kind of item carried by ladies of the Middle Ages.

GLOSSARY: PLAIN PIG TALK

There are a lot of different words to describe pigs. I am assuming that you are pretty new to this, so this is what it all means.

Barrow
A castrated male pig

Boar
An uncastrated male pig

Finisher
A young pig that is nearing slaughter

Gilt
A female pig that hasn't yet produced a litter, or has had a litter that hasn't been weaned

Grower
A piglet after weaning

Hog
A castrated male pig

In pig
A female pig who is pregnant

Maiden
A sexually mature female pig who has not yet mated

Piglet
A young pig up to the weaning stage

Porker
A pig being raised for its meat

Sow

A female pig that has weaned a litter

Store pig

A pig between weaning and slaughter age

Suckling Pig

An unweaned piglet

Weaner

A newly-weaned piglet, around 8—10 weeks old